INSTRUCTOR'S MANUAL

Fitness
Through
Aerobics & Step Training

Karen S. Mazzeo, M.Ed.
Bowling Green State University

Morton Publishing Company
925 West Kenyon Avenue, Unit 12
Englewood, Colorado 80110

Contents

I.   How To Use The Instructor's Manual

Fitness • Through Aerobics & Step Training is an abridged edition of the author's text entitled, *Aerobics • The Way To Fitness* and has been developed to accompany your physical fitness course that includes aerobic exercise-dance, step/bench training, strength training primarily using light resistance means, and flexibility training. It is written for the beginner, progressing to the intermediate or advanced status in both fitness and skill level, within the time-frame of up to 30 class meetings.

The author of this fitness text and instructor's manual has over twenty years of teaching experience, primarily at the university level. The ideas presented here are the tested methods for effectively teaching large numbers of students.

Enjoy the time-saving, creative ideas that have been compiled for your convenience. You are invited to use the forms and charts within this manual to more easily facilitate your preparation and continual management of the course, from the first to the last class meeting. There is a credit line on each page of this Instructor's Manual. Please be sure that it appears on any pages that are copied. This material is only for your classroom use.

The various ideas presented within this manual are in an order of probable use. Because of the variables present, you will have to adapt the ideas and order of presentation to your individual program setting.

II.   Lesson Progression For Teaching Using *Fitness • Through Aerobics & Step Training*

The following is a suggested progression for teaching/facilitating fitness fundamentals through the exercise modalities of aerobic exercise-dance and step/bench training, *plus as many total fitness basics you choose to present or have time for (bracketed ["Optional"]*, based on 30 one-hour class meetings. As an aerobics and step training instructor, it is important to remember your dual roles, both as an educator and as a performer, having the ultimate goal of providing student independence from a formal class setting, to having the ability to enjoy engaging in aerobic exercise anywhere and anytime, alone or in a group setting.

Because all students will not begin the course at the same fitness or motor skill level, and will also tend to progress at different rates, you will need to make adjustments to this schedule of lessons and plan alternatives when it becomes necessary, for continual challenge to occur.

Note: You'll continually be referenced to Section III. of this manual for further clarity of lesson presentation methods identified within this thirty day plan. These additional method suggestions are listed on the *same day* as they are noted here, in order mentioned for that day: **Note:** III./day/order.

Also, as the lessons progress, just the *new* material is listed on the lesson days. Full workouts continue, using previously presented techniques.

DAY 1

▶ **Before class:** Have photocopies of IV.A, IV.B, V., and extra copies of Student Information Profile (for students without texts first day); one photocopy of IX and VI; bring extra pencils.

▶ Introduce self and course.

▶ **Social interaction:** Arrange yourselves in an alphabetized-circle order.

▶ Fill out Student Information Profile (located in Introduction of their text). This is for roster update and attendance purposes.

▶ Fill out IV.A Student Physical Activity Readiness. Identifies persons with limitations.

▶ Hand out and read aloud, IV.B Responsibilities of Student Participating in Aerobics/Step Training Exercise Class. Sign document *Your reading it and their signing acknowledging "understanding," affixes the responsibility with the student.*

▶ Collect the above three forms, stapling sets together (while students are in the alphabetized circle).

▶ Distribute V. Course Syllabus. Discuss all sections for clarity. **Note: III./1/1.**

▶ Enumerate VI. Course Objectives In Detail (or at beginning of Day 2).

▶ Give floor/space position assignment to each student (for future attendance purposes), using form IX. Attendance Made Easy.

▶ **Assignment:** Read Chapters 1 and 2 in text, which are the introduction to mental and physical fitness training, and bring text and a pencil to each class meeting. "Street clothes" appropriate for Day 2.

▶ **After class:** Record individual student's limitations to be aware of on IX., their attendance positions.

DAY 2

▶ **Before class:** Photocopy VIII. Have established and posted on your office door, one or two small group office hours, established specifically to update late additions to your class, regarding the filling out of the required paperwork.

▶ Attendance by "spot check" of vacant spaces on IX.

▶ Assign an attendance position to persons who just added the course and be sure to give a packet of all the paperwork distributed to students on Day 1. Tell them to sign up for a posted, "small group update," office hour appointment — ASAP, and before the next class meeting — to make up Day 1 required paperwork.

▶ [Enumerate VI. Course Objectives in Detail.]

▶ Invite students to be *continually considering* all of the fitness mindset information presented in Chapter 1 for the first several weeks of class. **Note: III./2/1.**

▶ Explain total fitness principles and definitions: **Note: III./2/2.**

▶ Demonstrate and detail 3 methods of monitoring exercise intensity. Mention ease that the 6-second count provides by just adding a "0." **Note: III./2/3.**

▶ **Assignment:** Begin to record five days of your RsHR for figuring TZHR next class meeting. **Note: III./2/4.**

▶ Administer VIII. Aerobics/Step Training Knowledge Pre-Test. Collect written tests and answer sheets alphabetically. **Note: III./2/5.**

▶ **Assignment:** Carefully read Chapter 3 — fitness testing procedures. Come dressed in fitness attire next class meeting.

DAY 3

▶ [**Before class:** Contact university public relations office and make arrangements for photographer to come to your class Day 4 and take two "large proof-sheet size" photos of each student; ask cost per each set of two.]

▶ Ask all students who are late additions to the class to see you, at onset of the hour. **Note: III./3/VIP NOTE.**

▶ Perform aerobic capacity fitness assessment using text Table 3.1 or 3.2, Cooper's 12 Minute or 1.5 Mile Running/Walking Test. **Note: III./3/1&2.**

▶ [Fitness test flexibility with the Sit & Reach Test and muscular endurance with Curl-Ups in 1 Minute Test. Procedures and values not given in the *Fitness Through Aerobics & Step Training* text or manual, but are in the text, *Aerobics • The Way to Fitness.*]

▶ Record results as attendance means for the day.

▶ Students place calculated RsHR average on *Fitness* text page 19, #3.

▶ Figure TZHR range on text page 19. **Note:** III./3/3.

▶ Determine 10 second count from Table 2.1 Target Heart Rate Training Zones, page 21 in text. **Note:** III./3/4.

▶ [Sign a "Personal Commitment Contract & Short Term Goal Setting" form that you design. **Note:** III./3/5.]

▶ **Assignments:** [Begin to record all aerobic workout modalities on form you develop entitled "Aerobics Log — Walking, Running, In-line Skating, or Cycling. **Note:** III./3/6.]

　✢ Read Chapter 6 — Safety First: Guidelines and Good Positioning. [Come dressed in clothing that reveals your physique. We'll be taking two posture photos: a side view and a back view. Bring cost to cover these two photos. **Note:** III./3/7.]

▶ **After class:** Have all data recorded and filed on each student, i.e., limitations; Knowledge Pre-Test score (recorded as +correct/50, or any number up to 50 that you choose to test them on); fitness field test laps / time / or / label: VP-P-F-G-E-S. Give each student an estimated "label" of "Beginner" / "Intermediate" / "Advanced" from VII. Identifying Student Skill Level & Rate of Progression. Place all data on each name's attendance square. Take this form to every class for quick reference.

DAY 4

▶ [**Before class:** Bring visuals necessary for successful posture photo session. **Note:** III./4/1.]

▶ Give results from VIII. Aerobics & Step Knowledge Pre-Test, Physical Fitness Field Test, and an estimated label ("Beginner" / "Intermediate" / "Advanced") for individual fitness and skill levels at start of this course (one-on-one, during your attendance taking).

▶ [Posture photo session. **Note:** III./4/2.]

▶ [Before photographer leaves, agree upon a date and time to pick up the large proof-size photos. They come about 9 per sheet and you need to cut.]

▶ Lecture on Chapter 6 Safety First: Guidelines and Good Positioning. Emphasize key points in each subtitle that are most important to your program, situation, and students: sensible training; overexertion; illness; missed sessions; locations and environment; shoe selection; proper clothing; fluids; common injuries; drug use; seek professional resources.

▶ Invite all questions and concerns about any points in the first half of Chapter 6 (up to good positioning). State openness to answering any questions relating to concerns or safety that may arise as course progresses.

▶ Lecture on good positioning/posture; the depth of the details you present will be relevant to your program needs.

▶ Practice good positioning/posture techniques. As you detail good positioning, students assume good posture: standing, lifting, lowering, and carrying. If you have step benches in your classroom, practice proper lifting/lowering/carrying techniques with these if they are part of your course. Proper step-bench positioning techniques can wait until step training is presented later on.

▶ Practice good dynamic positions by practicing awareness exercises in student text, plus others you add.

▶ If you need a "time filler," practice good dynamic positioning using the Bounce 'n Tap Series (Figure 7.12 a, b, c) which can be an excellent way to integrate posture principles while exercising.

▶ Provide cool-down walking the perimeter of the room for 2-3 minutes if the Bounce 'n Tap Series was performed for an extended period of time.

▶ **Assignments:** Practice good posture exercises, both static and dynamic, including lifting, lowering, and carrying. Re-read last half of Chapter 2, concerning impact.

▶ [Bring to class a low nutrient/high calorie food sample that equals 12 calories: 1 very large potato chip; or several multiples of 12 (24/36/48/60) like 1/5th of a candy bar (48 calories) that equals 240 calories.]

DAY 5

▶ [**Before class:** Bring a large bag of potato chips to class for visual aid for those who were absent/ forgot assignment.]

▶ Teach by both lecture and full demonstration/ participation the last half of Chapter 2 detailing various impact evaluation information: high / low / combo high-low / and moderate impact aerobics. **Note:** III./5/1.

▶ Detail caloric expenditure from aerobics research, and personalize expenditure and intake of energy with demonstration. **Note:** III./5/2.

▶ Provide cool-down walking for 2-3 minutes.

▶ Highlight chapter conclusion, welcoming *their* philosophies about exercising.

▶ **Assignment:** Practice varying aerobic impacts. Read Chapter 4 (principles), Chapter 7, sections 1 and 4 only (warm-up and cool-down techniques), and re-read Chapter 1 (the fitness mindset).

DAY 6

▶ [**Before class:** Copy and staple X. Self-Management: "What Do You Say When You Talk To Yourself?" Steps I-IV.]

▶ **Before class:** bring two large, thin rubber-bands to class (office supply type).

▶ Present overview of Chapter 4 — the principles involved in the segments of an aerobic

exercise-dance class: (1) warm-up / stretch; (2) aerobics; (3) strength training; (4) isolation exercises; cool-down, flexibility, relaxation.

▶ Give detailed explanation and demonstration of the methods of warming up and stretching, and cooling-down, incorporating flexibility training with relaxation using the exercise techniques in Chapters 4 and 7. **Note:** III./6/1.

▶ Integrate the fitness mindset information now by presenting the idea that there is a way to improve all segments of a fitness program — make improvements faster, safer, and in the most pleasurable way, and that is by incorporating their mind into their physical workout. Present concept of *motivation*, identified in block on page 11 of Chapter 2. **Note:** III./6/2, 3, 4, & 5.

▶ [Distribute X. Self-Management: "What Do You Say When You Talk To Yourself?," Steps I-IV. Begin listing information requested in Steps I & II only.

▶ **Assignments:** Practice all of the techniques presented today. (*Continue to assign practicing all of the physical segments of the aerobic workout every class hereafter.*) Review Chapters 4, section 2, and Chapter 7, section 2, the aerobic-dance exercise segment principles and techniques.

DAY 7

▶ [**Before class:** Pick up/pay for posture photos. **Note:** III./7/1.]

▶ Explain XII. Cueing Signs you'll be using. [Make a large poster visual to accompany your explanation; keep it permanently at teaching station.]

▶ Teach aerobics segment techniques: low-impact aerobics warm-up; power low-impact; high/low impact; varieties like funk aerobics; power low-impact; low-impact aerobics cool-down; post-aerobic stretching.

▶ Take at least two heart rate readings and estimate rates of perceived exertion. *Continue to do this monitoring every class, hereafter.*

▶ [Record readings of monitoring target heart rates and rates of perceived exertion. **Note:** III./7/2.]

▶ [Return posture photos to students and facilitate self-assessment of posture. Ask any students who have particular questions concerning their posture assessment to discuss privately after class, or during office hours.]

▶ **Assignments:** Practice all of the techniques learned in class. [Complete posture assessment and bring to class next meeting.]

　▶ Review Chapter 4, section 3 on strength training and calisthenics segment and Chapter 7, section 3 on strength training techniques. Bring 1-2 lb. light hand-held weights if you have them.

DAY 8

▶ **Before class:**

　▶ Write a memo to students summarizing all the written monitoring and charting they are to be continually doing on an ongoing basis. (Since a wide variety of "option" opportunities have been given, for you to tailor-make the course to your preference, this update will consist of choices you've made for them to experience.)

　▶ Bring commercial resistance bands and tubing for students; and one pair of 1-2 lb. hand-held weights.

▶ [Review points of good positioning and how they measured up on their self-assessment.]

▶ Teach information concerning orthotics (text pages 60-61), if assessment (self/or instructor observation) of any/several students warrants it.

▶ Conclude posture information with key point that good body positioning will be stressed during *all* exercise technique taught during course. Mention that the *only* way

hand-weights will be allowed during aerobic exercise (dance or step) is if the individual can maintain good positioning continually throughout the workout. No exceptions.

▶ Perform warm-up stretching for five minutes.

▶ Teach strength training segment principles and techniques, in depth: text pages 39–44; ACSM Guidelines; perform exercises for upper body (chest, upper back, shoulders, and arms); mid section (abdominals, lower back); lower body (hips and buttocks, thighs, and lower legs), pages 94-95. **Note:** III./8/1.

▶ Facilitate teaching each isolated muscle group using various light weight resistances: bands, tubing, 1-2 lb. hand-held weights (if equipment is present), and your own body as the weight resistance used. (Hold off using the bench exercises until after bench information has been presented.)

▶ Perform cool-down stretching for 5 minutes following strength training exercises.

▶ Students record in their textbook on page 104. **Note:** III./8/2.

▶ **Assignment:** Practice all techniques presented today. Review Chapter 1, Anchoring a Fitness Mindset.

　▶ [Have completed X. Self-Management, Sections I. & II., and bring to next class.]

DAY 9

▶ Facilitate a full workout session emphasizing good posture during each segment: warm-up and stretching, aerobic exercise-dance, two or three heart rate monitorings, strength training, cool-down, and concluding with static stretching with brief relaxation techniques, consisting of images, affirmations, and breathing that all promote recovery and rejuvenation.

▶ Facilitate the information collected on the X. Self-Management form, or the ideas they thought about, if it was not a written assignment.

▶ Discuss the fitness mindset self-talk they've been using and how to now restructure the negative into positive talk.
   ▶ [Do Step III of X. and have it completed by next class.]
▶ Ask input on their observations of others self-speak and media talk. They will begin to realize how they are mentally programmed and need to intervene with new beliefs if positive, permanent change is going to occur.
▶ Discuss positive fitness beliefs and how to re-word old worn out beliefs that are disabling to their fitness mindset.
▶ **Assignment:** Re-structure negative self-talk and beliefs into positive self-talk and beliefs, Step III. of X. Self-Management. Come with updated "programming" to next class.

DAY 10

▶ [**Before class:** Take one copy of X. Self-Management, Step IV; or have it made into an overhead transparency or chart from which to facilitate the presentation.]
▶ [Facilitate X. Self-Management Step IV., Making Your Own Reprogramming- For-Improvement Tape On Your Behaviors, Emotions, Attitudes, & Beliefs. **Note:** III./10/1.]
▶ **Assignment:** Read Chapter 9, Stress Management Principles and Relaxation Techniques.

DAY 11

▶ Teach Chapter 9, Stress Management Principles and Relaxation Techniques. **Note:** III./11/1.
▶ [Reflect upon your stress outlets. Facilitate the possible coping behaviors we personally enjoy, and consider the triggers that set off the behavior.]
▶ Facilitate relaxation using the guided imagery technique, Total Body Scanning, for a maximum of three minutes, this first time,

accomplishing just Steps 1, 2, and 4 (position, deep breathing, heart rate monitoring, and a *must* is the stretch alert). **Note:** III./11/2 & 3.
▶ *Facilitate at least 3 minutes of relaxation every class, hereafter, every time sustained, high-intensity exercise is performed.*
▶ **Assignments:**
   ▶ Practice relaxation techniques daily when needed and also at bedtime. (*Continue to assign practicing relaxation techniques every class hereafter.*)
   ▶ Read Chapter 5, Enjoyment Through Aerobic Varieties, bench/step training principles, plus page 69, Step Training Postures, and Chapter 7 Bench/Step Training techniques: bench/step direction approaches and base steps.
   ▶ [Bring a jump rope to class.]

DAY 12

▶ **Before class:** Make arrangements for step/benches to be available in classroom. [Bring jump rope to demonstrate — one for everyone if all are to use.]
▶ Aerobic exercise varieties: step/bench training; pace walking; jumping rope.
▶ Teach Chapter 5 — bench/step training principles: definitions and benefits; choosing your bench height; music; proper body alignment and stepping technique; common errors to avoid (p. 69); step technique progression; safety concerns; briefly mention adding hand-held weights but tell them this is an advanced option added in a few weeks and fully discussed then; adjusting your intensity; review correct lifting, lowering, and carrying of the bench (p. 70).
▶ Teach directional approaches/bench orientation. (Omit all arms today; hands constantly on hips.)
▶ Teach — jumping rope principles (text pp. 54-56). [Perform varieties.]

▶ Teach — pace walking principles (text pp. 54-55). Integrate this as an active warm-up or cool-down then, throughout the course; encourage pace walking as an alternate weekly fitness modality.

▶ Provide cool-down, post-stretch, and brief relaxation technique.

▶ **Assignments:**

   ▶ Fill out Relaxed/Tensed Control Panel With One Large Dial, on student text page 124. Be sure to place how they feel today — give "today" a quantified number.

   ▶ Read Chapter 7, Bench/Step Training Techniques, Base Steps.

DAY 13

▶ Perform warm-up/stretch involving the step/bench, especially involving the lower body — buttocks, legs, ankles, feet. (Adapt the aerobics warm-up stretching techniques, now to include the bench.)

▶ Give update suggestions for self-talk affirmations to accompany warm-up stretching, using this new exercise modality (i.e., l-o-n-g, w-a-r-m glutes, hamstrings, calves and heel cords).

▶ Review, and add any new, visual and verbal cueing you will be using.

▶ Begin teaching bench approaches/orientation for the base steps: single lead step, alternating lead step (using bench tap, floor tap, lunge back), and step touch toe and heel taps.

▶ Provide a cool-down, incorporating the base step Step Touch, using both the toe and heel for the touching.

▶ Facilitate relaxation using the guided imagery technique, Total Body Scanning, adding Step 3. Provide technique taking up to 5 minutes.

▶ Discuss their responses regarding how they filled out the Relaxed/Tensed Control Panel With One Large Dial, p. 124.

▶ **Assignments:** Practice all step training techniques presented (*Continue to always assign practicing new step training techniques presented every class.*)

DAY 14

▶ Continue teaching bench approaches/orientation for the base steps.

▶ As you practice base steps, begin adding low-range arm movements (elbows kept near waist/sides).

▶ **Assignments:** Practice all new step and arm techniques. Review all assigned course reading and the skills presented for mid-term testing/review. (Clarify the type of mid-term testing/review you are using: written, motor skills, both, or just a review of all techniques.)

DAY 15

▶ **Before class:** Copy option(s) you choose to use as midterm examination. Pre-number each written exam copy; bring "bubble" answer sheets for written exams.

▶ **Mid-term options:**

   ▶ Select key questions from the XVII. Final Examination and use as the midterm exam.

   ▶ Separate final examination into two halves, and give the first half only, as the midterm examination and the second half only, as the final examination.

   ▶ Test performance of motor skills using XVI. Fitness Course Instructor Evaluation of Students/And Student Self-Assessment. **Note:** III./15/1.

   ▶ Facilitate XVI. as a Student Self-Assessment Of Techniques/Skills/Key Knowledge. (No "testing," just a reviewing of all techniques presented; students given time to check off techniques they've personally mastered.)

▶ **Assignment:** Read Chapter 7, Bench/Step Training Basic Step Patterns (up to Variations of Base Steps and Basic Step Patterns).

▶ **After class:** Grade and record written exams. Analyze most missed information and re-teach these points during opportune moments, the remainder of the term.

DAY 16

▶ **Before class:** Establish procedure/time/day for make-up of the midterm exam.

▶ Announce office hour(s) that midterm exam can be made up, before next class.

▶ Teach basic step patterns: v-step, bypass moves (variations of base steps).

▶ Add middle-range arm movements (elbows are kept chest/shoulder high or lower).

DAY 17

▶ Distribute results of mid-term written/skill testing as means of attendance taking. Go over information. Re-collect.

▶ Teach basic step patterns: straddle down and straddle up.

▶ Add high-range arm movements (elbows are shoulder/above the shoulder high). Present this arm movement option, but limit the number of high-range arm movements and repetitions. **Note:** III./17/1.

▶ **Assignment:** Read Chapter 7, Bench/Step Training Techniques, Variations of Base Steps & Basic Step Patterns.

DAY 18

▶ Teach variations: combining base steps and basic step patterns, like the traveling patterns that use both the length and width of the bench.

▶ Add all range-levels of arm movements.

DAY 19

▶ Teach repeaters.

▶ Vary directional approaches for base steps and basic step patterns.

▶ Explain schematic of writing out a step pattern and perform the pattern variation, From The End, on student text, page 91.

DAY 20

▶ Teach propulsion steps (used with tap step, lunge step, and adding a hop to bypass and traveling moves).

▶ Invite those who have 1-4 lb. hand-held weights to bring them next time.

DAY 21

▶ Present ways to vary intensity. **Note:** III./21/1.

▶ Facilitate adding 1-4 lb. hand-held weights to step training. Review pages 52-53.

▶ **Assignment:** Read Chapter 7, Section 3, Strength Training, focusing on the techniques that use the bench platform in level, incline and decline positions using resistance tubing or your body as the weight.

DAY 22

▶ Present all the strength exercises mentioned in text that use the bench and tubing. Facilitate it as a "step and strength" interval program: 3 minutes step / 1 minute strength, using the tubing. Be sure knees are bent during the action phase of the strength interval, to retain high intensity heart rates.

▶ **Assignment:** Read Chapter 10, Eating For Fitness.

DAY 23

▶ Step with strength workout.

▶ Eating strategies lecture. **Note:** III./23/1.

▶ **Assignments:** [Monitor and record your food and drink for two weeks. **Note:** III./23/2].

▶ Read Chapter 11, Positive Weight Management and Chapter 8, Choreography.

DAY 24

▶ **Before class:** Set up times and bring sign-up sheet for body composition assessment testing each student using skinfold technique, in the exercise physiology lab (performed by technicians), or your office (performed by you).

▶ Present information on body composition and how assessment is performed. **Note:** III./24/1.

▶ Invite students to have body composition assessed by skinfolding technique; instruct them how to dress for it and where to go to have it performed. Sign up for appointed time during class.

▶ Present principles for aerobics choreography by performing it as you lecture.

▶ Use text Table 8.1 on page 113 to plan.

DAY 25

▶ **Before class:** Obtain XV. Body Composition Assessments and record 3 skinfold readings on each student for your records.

▶ Bring XV. forms to class, alphabetized for easy distribution.

▶ Give out and interpret XV. Body Composition Assessment readings, review body lean and body fat highlights, and facilitate figuring out the assessment.

▶ Present concepts of "health fitness" / "high physical fitness" standards.

▶ Challenge individuals to now set/maintain a goal (on XV.) regarding their weight in terms of percent body fat that is of a "high physical fitness" standard. Present principles for step aerobics choreography, performing as you lecture.

▶ Use text Table 8.2 Creating Your Own Step Training Pattern Variations to plan. **Note:** III./25/1.

DAY 26

▶ **Before class:** Bring fat visual aid to class.

▶ Weight management lecture. **Note:** III./26/1.

▶ Introduce XIV. Motivational Theme Classes. **Note:** III./26/2 & 3.

▶ **Assignment**: [Make an Eating Control Panel With One Large Dial (similar to the visual in student text on page 124, but now representing "empty" and "full" and used as an eating

strategy). **Important:** Use your *own* labels for the numbers. Bring to next class. **Note:** III./26/4]

DAY 27

▶ Ask for student's new ideas either for their Eating Control Panel With One Large Dial, or for the list of labels given in their student text on page 144.

▶ Group demonstrations. **Note:** III./27/1.

▶ **During/after class:** Record all sequences and creative theme ideas students portrayed/demonstrated, for your own future use.

DAY 28

▶ **Before class:** Bring XVI. Fitness Course Instructor Evaluation of Students.

▶ Options for this session:
  ▶ Group demonstrations continued.
  ▶ XIII. Aerobics and Step Circuit Training.
  ▶ Review of all aerobics and step training steps, patterns, and sequences.
  ▶ XVI. Fitness Course Instructor Evaluation of Students. **Note:** III./28/1.

▶ **Assignment:** Bring all written assignments being evaluated for course grade to next class.

DAY 29

▶ [**Before class:** copy XVIII.]

▶ Collect any assignments that were chosen to be evaluated as part of course.

▶ Post-testing of physical fitness (Table 3.1 or 3.2 in text). **Note:** III./28 & 29/1.

▶ Record physical fitness post-test results on attendance position.

▶ [XVIII. Self Post-Assessment of all fitness facets. Collect.]

▶ Fill out Priorities and Goals, Chapter 12 in text.

▶ Indicate format to be followed during the last class.

DAY 30

▶ **Before class:** Compile data of numbers of changes +/− in physical fitness values assessed and collected. Copy XVII. (only the questions you choose to use). Pre-number each final exam. Bring computer "bubble" answer sheets and extra pencils. Copy XIX. (only preferred version: (XIX.A) subjective or (XIX.B) objective.

▶ Return collected assignments.

▶ Present collected data values of change experienced in this class. Encourage life-long participation in *Fitness Through Aerobics & Step Training* concepts.

▶ **Final Examination:** Give computer "bubble" answer sheet forms first; fill out requested data.

▶ Give pre-numbered test copy to each student and they record that number on their answer sheet; they write nothing on the test, just on the answer sheet.

▶ [Provide bonus points for listing (on prepared or blank sheet of paper given with exam) their

priorities and goals set, as established in text, Chapter 12.]

▶ Collect exams and answer sheets at the same time, one-on-one when student is finished.

▶ Mention you will turn in their grades *before* reading the class's course and instructor evaluations.

▶ Distribute XIX.A/ or B Course & Instructor Evaluation form after exam is turned in, one-on-one to each student. Student places anonymous evaluation in large envelope near exit when leaving.

▶ **After class:** After evaluating, recording, and turning in grades issued, read and record all evaluations. Immediately use the constructive criticism to improve the course and your teaching methods. Since direct comments and suggestions are given on the XIX.A subjective evaluation instrument, for personal growth and improvement, this type of form is usually more constructive and helpful to you.

▶ **Note:** III./1-30/1.

III. Facilitating the Text's Tables & Charts, Plus Suggested Classroom Methodologies to Use

To ease class management, especially when you are given large numbers of students, the following hints, shortcuts, and methods are given, in addition to those already presented in Section II. of this Instructor's Manual. They may not always directly apply to your circumstances or environment, so adaptation will be necessary on your part. They coincide with the *day* the material is suggested to be presented, as found in Section II.

DAY 1

#1　The syllabus is designed to reflect *what exactly students can expect from you* and also *what exactly you expect from each student.* Clarifying all

of your (and your department's) policies very specifically on paper helps to prevent all misinterpretation problems that may try to arise during the term. It is key that each student be given this document *Day One*, and all their questions answered then.

DAY 2

#1　It is key to assign the Chapter 1 reading at the onset of the course to get students *thinking* about mental training, but wait several weeks to present "Anchoring A Fitness Mindset" in depth with lecture and worksheets. Facilitate this chapter when it is directly usable, which can be when you discuss how self-talk affirmations accompany the warm-up/stretching segment on Day 5. By waiting, students are much more receptive to learning how to make permanent positive improvement, in the shortest period of time.

#2 Be sure to cover all of these principles: aerobic/aerobics/aerobic exercise-dance; aerobic fitness; flexibility; muscular strength and endurance; posture; and body composition. Define aerobic capacity; progressive overload. Enumerate aerobic modality alternatives. Detail aerobic criteria.

#3 Figure 2.4 The Borg Scale: Ratings Of Perceived Exertion (RPE)

▶ Briefly teach the RPE concept at this point, but then be sure to cover it again, in depth, *after* the presentation on Target Heart Rate Training Zone and pulse readings.

▶ Later, after the RPE is presented in depth, frequently ask students the "number" they're feeling during the workout sessions the remainder of the course. Liken the peak performance "5" to feeling warm, a full sweat, breathing continually and with ease, and feeling great!

#4 Plotting Resting Heart Rate

▶ Key directions are on page 18 of the student text. Additionally, keep a timepiece near your bed without an alarm clock ring. If digital is used, wait until a new minute has clocked over; take pulse until time clicks again.

#5 VIII. Aerobics & Step Training Knowledge Pre-test

▶ This survey test can be *read* to all, with students using just computer "bubble" answer sheets; or distributed as a *written* test, with accompanying "bubble" answer sheets.

▶ If you pass out the written test, number each pre-test and have student place that number on their "bubble" answer sheet. Hand both in

together. This procedure secures all your test instruments.

▶ Do not go over the answers at this point in course.

DAY 3

#VIP (Very Important Procedure) Note: Do not allow any students to take the aerobic capacity fitness assessment test who are late additions to the class, if they have not filled out the paperwork distributed on Day 1. The reasoning for this involves your professional liability.

▶ Most universities do not require students to have physical examinations prior to participation in fitness classes. Therefore, you need to take two actions: (a) become aware of the high-risk history and behaviors background information on each student, and (b) affix responsibility for assumption of risk upon the student. This is accomplished by them filling out their personal information and you reading the responsibility form to the students aloud, followed by them signing their name that they "understand" the assumption of risk they are taking, by enrolling in your class.

▶ Students who, therefore, were not present for the initial paperwork of the course are invited to leave class now, and sign up for an office hour time frame on your office door — ASAP — to complete the required forms.

▶ All class meetings they miss are marked as "absent" until this is done. Refer to your course syllabus distributed to them.

▶ You may then wish to provide an aerobic capacity fitness test assessment make-up date for all who miss the testing procedures and information given on Day 3.

#1 Table 3.1 Cooper's 12 Minute Walking/ Running Test

▶ The Field Test of Fitness is easily managed within the classroom, IF pre-planning is thought through.

▶ It is easiest in the large class setting to perform the test using Table 3.1 (the 12 Minute Test), because you can manage the variable of class time allotted to perform the test (i.e., 12 minutes from start to stop).

▶ Each student gets a partner to hold their text and mark full and partial laps performed, which equal the distances described in Cooper's Table. *You need to know ahead of time how many laps, and partial laps, of your facility or track equal certain distances (like one mile and portions of a mile).*

▶ Give partners the choice of who goes first. If a student has an important class/meeting/etc. directly after your class, suggest this partner goes first in order that they feel fully recovered and revitalized before their next appointment.

▶ While the first group is taking the test, all of the partners who are recording sit together in the same area, near the instructor, who is the official time-keeper. During the run, coach the sitting partner to carefully watch their partner who is running, for signs of problems, accurately counting their laps, and giving encouragement each time they pass by. Use this "down" time to teach key principles to those who are sitting and recording.

▶ When the test is over, be sure everyone stops the test (both taking and recording) at the 12-minute stop signal. Encourage the runners to continue to cool-down and walk for at least 2-3 minutes. Research tells us if problems are likely to occur with fitness testing it is *directly afterwards.* So insist that each student engages in a cool-down walk. During this time, the recording partners figure their runner's results and then begin to warm-up and stretch. When the first group of runners have cooled down, the new runners give partner their texts to record their laps now.

▶ Begin the second group of runners all together at the same starting location and at the same time. Present key fitness principles to the new group sitting. End second group at 12 minutes, and again require a 2-3 minute cool-down by slow walking.

#2   Table 3.2 Cooper's 1.5 Mile Walking/Running Test

▶ This version of the Field Test Of Fitness can be managed in much the same way as the 12 minute run with these exceptions: The partner sitting counts the number of laps (predetermined by you) and then *they* determine when their individual runner's stop time is, by when their runner has completed the 1.5 mile distance. One of these options must be present: (1) one large visual time piece is needed; (2) all the sitting partners need individual timepieces to record their runner with accuracy; or (3) the instructor needs to constantly call out the length of time it has taken, after the first runner crosses the 1.5 mile completion mark.

▶ This test version does not provide for an effective class time management, so be aware that this test may take much longer to facilitate in the classroom setting (i.e., it may take some students in both trials, 20 minutes to finish 1.5 miles).

#3   How To Figure Your Target Heart Rate Training Zone (TZHR)

▶ The resting heart rate has to be figured for five consecutive days before this formula can be accurately figured, so be sure the RsHR assignment precedes figuring TZHR.

▶ Figure this formula in class, all together at the same time, to eliminate any confusion.

▶ The results of this information (knowing your personal TZHR) is key to the student understanding many aerobic principles. Be sure you see their figuring, or ask them what their range is, at some early point in the course.

#4   Table 2.1 TZHR's — Pulse Beats Counted In 10 Seconds

▶ Students must have completed figuring their RsHR average before an accurate 10-second-count range can be assumed.

#5 Develop a form entitled, "Personal Commitment & Short-Term Goal Setting."

▶ Encourage students to set commitments and short-term goals that are concrete and *very specific*, so that each can be immediately experienced as to whether or not follow-through is occurring.

▶ Establishing goals for some of the goal possibilities you design on this form may be an area of "extra credit" for this course. Student would have to be tested outside of the class for most of the values (i.e., cholesterol readings; daily caloric intake and expenditure; body composition; flexibility sit and reach testing; muscular endurance of the abdominals; etc.) then researching — on their own — how to change the value they are at, to achieve a more positive result. A brief research paper could accompany the goal setting/achieving, to facilitate issuing the "extra credit."

#6 Logging Weekly Participation In Aerobic Exercise Alternatives

▶ Encourage students to exercise cardiovascularly at least three times per week, practicing the skills taught in class, *or* develop enjoyment in alternative modalities that will develop cardiovascular fitness and assist with the other fitness goals students have set.

▶ Point out that having a wide variety of exercise modes will curb "exercise boredom" for a lifetime!

▶ Recording this information on a regular basis may be considered a "bonus option" for course evaluation.

#7 Posture photo preparation: Students will receive two 3" × 2" photos to compare with the characteristics of both poor and good posture, on pages 67 and 68 of student text. The $1.00-2.00 (usual fee per student) covers cost of labor, film developing, and two proof-size photos. Come with *exact* cost.

▶ In order to clearly see your posture so it's not a waste of time/money, come wearing lycra/Spandex®, leotard, or a swim suit and you'll be taking off your shoes and socks. Come with long hair tied up, so shoulder line shows. Entire procedure takes about 10-20 seconds per student.

DAY 4

#1 Before class: Make two sets of index cards with the numbers 0-9 on each set. These will be placed on the floor near the feet. As students sign a numbered sheet and pay, that same number is set on index cards; when photos are returned to you, you know exactly how to distribute photos by the numbers.

▶ Place one foot strip of masking tape on floor to represent where student is to stand for the two shots. Bring extra ribbon/tie along, to tie up long hair. Ask trustworthy student to facilitate the signing up and collecting cost of photos, so you are free to direct the photo session.

#2 During class: Show students the rapid procedure of the session by first having your own photos taken. Use these photos as future visuals to explain procedure and what you're looking for, so take "good" and "poor" posture photos of yourself.

DAY 5

#1 Students will be very anxious for a full session of working out, so it is important to demonstrate and lecture simultaneously, while they mirror what you are doing. All aerobic impact work is taught with high intensity (i.e., working in the TZHR), but the music you choose to background your teaching should be only slow-to-moderate tempo, so that the different impacts can be realized.

#2 It is impressive to **experience** equating expending 12 calories per minute of high intensity aerobic exercise (whether it is high/low/combo/or moderate impact), to the eating of various low nutrient/high calorie food like one very large potato chip; or exercising for four minutes (i.e., 48 calories) and consuming one bite (1/5th) of a candy bar that contains 240 total calories.

▶ Experiencing either of these examples is most effective if the exercise is done first, and the chip or bite of a candy bar is eaten afterwards.

▶ If this method is used, ask them to bring a low nutrient/high calorie food visual equalling 12 calories or several multiples of 12 (24/36/48/60). Provide a workout equivalent, and ask them to internalize the key point to be learned: the physical expenditure effort it takes to equal the food energy they ate.

DAY 6

#1   An excellent visual aid to use for teaching proper stretching technique is to use a thin rubber band (the office supply type) showing static stretching of muscles = a slow, taunt, stretched band; incorrect warm-up stretching = ballistic bouncing stretching, where tearing occurs with your minute muscle fibers (and the rubber band). Scarring will ensue, with less flexibility.

#2   Fitness mindset is best taught with visual aids shown in the text: a chart identifying the Self Management Model, an apple sliced in half so that the core and seeds show, a controlling forces pain/pleasure visual, a chart listing positive and negative verbs, enabling and disabling physiologies, and mental images that are, or are not, positively motivating.

#3   Internal motivation is an exciting concept and is taught in depth in the books that include neurolinguistic programming, as mentioned in the references.

#4   Giving the examples of attitude components that accompany stretching helps to make this information real and usable to the student now. Briefly **stating and picturing** to oneself that muscles are becoming "wider-longer-warmer-and full of energizing nutrients" is a start with mental training.

#5   More gains will then be achieved later, during the cool-down stretching phase when tension is being released and the ability to **focus** on pictures and self-talk becomes easier, for the novice of mental training. (It is always easier to focus on relaxing after heavy physical exertion.)

DAY 7

#1   Cut photo sets apart and put in alphabetical order for easy distribution. Identify any outstanding posture problems and make a note to discuss correction possibilities with students, one-on-one after they've had the opportunity to self-assess their photo.

#2   Monitoring THR & RPE: Have students record down (on inside back cover of their text) the pulses they feel and their RPE immediately after you take it, keeping all texts and pencils on perimeter of room for safety.

▶ Monitor exercise exertion at least two times during the workout session to be sure all are working in their TZHR. Initially during the learning process, recording THR down helps to equate actual pulse beats felt and transferring that actual felt physiology to the abstract idea of how hard you **think** you're working, on the RPE.

▶ Point out that people who are ill/recovering from injury/highly distressed will read unusually high heart rates with less than the usual exertion. If this is the case, pace your workout wisely. This is where your responsibility for your own exertion comes in, as signed on the hold-harmless, form IV.-B.

DAY 8

#1 Principles for strength training. An excellent visual aid to use for muscle fiber thickening (hypertrophy) is to show a thin rubber band = before weight/strength training, and a thick rubber band = after a regular, continual program of weight/strength training.

▶ Present anatomical names of muscles and the exercises that train specific muscle groups.

#2 Student textbook, page 104: Strength Training with Bands, Tubing, Light (1-4 lb.) Free Weights and Tubing with the Bench. Students list eight to ten of their favorite strength training exercises presented (targeting all major muscle groups) that they plan to continue. [When this page's entries are filled, continue recording in a journal.]

DAY 10

#1 **X. Self-Management, Step IV: Making Your Own Re-programming-For-Improvement Tape:**

▶ On Your Behaviors, Emotions, Attitudes, & Beliefs. Making an audio-tape can be a superior way to issue "extra-credit" for an activity they'll not only totally enjoy doing, but also they will never forget how powerful this behavior changing technique is, now and in the future when other changes are needed.

DAY 11

#1 Stress management lecture. Effective visual aids for stress concept is to use thin rubber band representing guitar strings, or a balloon. Wimpy condition = no challenges or stress; balanced tension = stretched band/inflated balloon; over-stressed = over-stretched, tearing or popping.

#2 When facilitating relaxation techniques, do only a short session the first time. You can read the technique slowly from the student text if you have a microphone, or record it on an audio-tape and play it in class. Either way works equally fine.

#3 Take an instructor facilitated heart rate reading *before and after* relaxation techniques. Compare the two readings. Emphasize the rejuvenation that occurs when relaxation ends a workout.

DAY 15

#1 **XVI. Fitness Course Instructor Evaluation Of Students.**

▶ This can be easily facilitated by asking students to continually move to the front of their attendance row every 30 seconds-to-one minute, and rotate then to the back of their line. Evaluate students in the front row or front bench positions.

DAY 17

#1 Upper-range arm movements. Because arm movements classified as upper-range tend to escalate the heart rate higher than the accompanying work reflects, it is advised to *limit* the number of upper-range movements you perform. There are enough methods to escalate intensity to challenge your workload, rather than performing continual upper-range arm movements.

DAY 21

#1 How to vary intensity. Intensity can be increased or decreased to accommodate your student's individual needs (regarding fitness, skill, health status, or goals) by changing any of the following variables: *raising or lowering the bench height; *adding or subtracting the use of hand-held weights; *using long- or short-levers; *using high- or low-impact steps; *using difficult or easy arm movement range-of-motion levels; *increasing or decreasing the music tempo or beats per minute.

DAY 23

#1 Eating strategies lecture. Bring an example of real food visuals, sealed in zip and lock bags, in correct "serving" proportions, all easily carried to class in a used suitcase (obtained from garage sales). Include a table cloth to set on the gym floor and a dried flowers centerpiece (visual presentation is key). Bring 1 cup and 1/2 cup measuring cups and dishes.

▶ Actually measuring food amounts for a lifetime is not a reasonable goal to set. Instead, teach how much 1 cup and 1/2 cup of specific food choices fit into what size of dish/bowl/plate/or cup. Begin to learn how to measure food *with your eyes* before eating. Seeing that a *cup* of salad fits into a small *pudding* type dish is a terrific realization; or the real shocker is that a 1/2 cup serving of cooked spaghetti is *not* the same as the huge plateful of spaghetti we usually eat.

#2 Fitness Eating — Monitoring Daily Consumption.

▶ When monitoring food and drink be sure to estimate consumption in the form of "servings." Remember to include all consumption each 24 hours.

DAY 24

#1   Body composition assessment using the skinfolding technique takes only moments to do, but with a large class it'll take an entire class session. Better time management may be to perform them during established office hour times or pre-scheduled in your department's exercise physiology lab, using XV. Body Composition Assessment By Skinfolding Technique. This form can be photocopied and given to lab, so the technician can mark down the three recordings directly for each student. You collect all forms from the lab, distribute in class, and go over procedure.

▶ If performed in the lab, have the technician *keep* the results and give them all to you at one time to distribute in class. This will enable you to explain the results all at one time, rather than asking the technician to repeat how to interpret individual readings received.

▶ Be sure students are made aware of where (on their body) the skinfold sights are to be measured, so that they will be appropriately dressed in tee shirt and shorts for easy assessment.

DAY 25

#1   Table 8.2 Creating Your Own Step Training Pattern Variations, page 114.

▶ People are one of your greatest resources! Be sure to review this Table from all of your students. It will provide you with an unlimited supply of fresh new variations, for both the present course and future courses. Note: XI. A Step Training Planning Page is provided for instructors to develop choreography for their classes.

DAY 26

#1   Weight management lecture.

▶ An effective visual aid is to bring one pound of fat (from the butcher shop) in a sealed bag and explain/demonstrate the exercise expenditure needed to metabolize one pound of (i.e., or any portion thereof) body fat.

#2   XIV. Motivational Theme Classes.

▶ Come "character" dressed today (instructor) and represent one of your own personal favorite themes.

▶ Be sure to take full advantage of every possible celebration and theme during your 10-15 weeks of class. It sparks and fuels a great amount of enthusiasm and positive energy on theme days! And, before the course is over, provide at least one opportunity to be creative with themes.

#3   Divide class into groups of 4 and ask each group to come up with a "theme" idea for next class. Assignment: Bring theme idea for a group demonstration and four visual aids — one for each member of your group to wear. Instructors who desire to encourage and generate a lot of creativity, do not do the option of dividing the group into 4's until next class. Have *each* student responsible for one theme and four visual aids for their group to perform/wear.

#4 Make a Control Panel With One Large Dial — An Eating Strategy for "empty" to "full."

▶ Find out and record unique new ways of interpreting the columns, from your students ideas!

DAY 27

#1 Group demonstrations.

▶ Divide class into groups of 4 and ask them to develop a multiple skill sequence to demonstrate to the class (aerobics, step training, or a combination of both). Integrate one or all of the theme ideas prepared for each group. Each group presents, then each group teaches the entire class their sequence (using/wearing the theme visual aids).

DAY 28

#1 XVI. Fitness Course Instructor Evaluation Of Students.

▶ If students were skill tested at midterm, complete the testing of the skills taught the second half of the course. If skills were not evaluated at midterm, this is a good time to do all of the skills testing.

DAY 28 & 29

#1 Table 3.1 or 3.2 Post-Testing Physical Fitness, Using Field Test Of Fitness.

▶ If you don't have the time available to post-test students' physical fitness, assign this post-test (on Day 28 or 29) as "homework" for students to do, and come with their results to the last class meeting. Ask students to pair up with a classmate and test one another, during a mutually agreeable time.

DAY 1-30

#1 Instructor Attitude.

▶ Always remember to be *personally and professionally "inviting"* — in your smile, your comments, the apparel you wear, the environmental conditions you can control, the music you choose, the policies you establish, and the program you offer. *You can make a difference.* The only collegiate physical education fitness experience some students will ever have, will be what *you* give to them.

Enjoy Being "Intentionally Inviting!"

IV.   Information Gathering

It is very important to know exactly who is taking your course, a brief profile background on each student, any limitations they have at the onset of the course so that you are aware of any unusual response certain individuals might have to the exercise you're directing, and after having given and read the responsibilities each student assumes, have their signed hold-harmless document in hand, and on file.

This three-document "bookkeeping" task is absolutely vital for your safe administration of the course. Take time to be methodical about collecting and reviewing each student's data and recording information on the attendance position as earlier noted, before *any* physical exertion is performed in class.

STUDENT INFORMATION PROFILE. This is located in student's textbook on page 3. For your convenience, photocopy this profile in order to have extra copies on hand for students who don't have a copy of the textbook, on Day #1.

IV.-A   Student Physical Activity Readiness

(**NOTE:** The purpose for this questionnaire is to serve as part of pre-screening for both fitness testing and exercise participation. If you respond "Yes" to any question, your instructor will want to talk further to you.)

	YES	NO
1. Has your doctor ever said that you have heart trouble?	_____	_____
2. Do you frequently suffer from pain in your chest or heart, especially with exercise?	_____	_____
3. Do you often feel faint or have spells of severe dizziness? More so with exercise?	_____	_____
4. Has your doctor ever told you that you have high blood pressure?	_____	_____
5. Have you ever been told you have a heart murmur?	_____	_____
6. Has a doctor ever told you that you have a bone or joint problem such as arthritis that has been aggrevated by exercise, or might be made worse by exercise?	_____	_____
7. Do you have diabetes mellitus?	_____	_____
8. Are you over 35 and unaccustomed to vigorous exercise?	_____	_____
9. Are you taking any medications or other drugs that might alter your response to exercise?	_____	_____
10. Are you pregnant?	_____	_____
11. Are you a smoker?	_____	_____
12. Have you recently had surgery, are obese, or have special limitations?	_____	_____
13. Do you have an at-risk cholesterol reading?	_____	_____
14. Do you have an abnormal resting ECG?	_____	_____
15. Do you have any family history of coronary disease, before or by age 50?	_____	_____
16. Is there a good physical reason not mentioned here why you should not follow an activity program, even if you wanted to?	_____	_____

If you answered "YES" to any question, please provide a brief explanation: (Use attached sheet if necessary.)
I have answered the above questions to the best of my knowledge.

_____/_____/_____
Print Name   Signature   Date

IV.-B Responsibilities Of Student Participating In An Aerobics Exercise/Step Training Class

INTRODUCTION

You have chosen to enroll in this course and having done so, it involves your physically active participation. This activity will involve certain risks, risks of which you are mindful, and which you have assumed. For your own safe participation in this course, you are asked to carefully review this form entitled, "Responsibilities of Student Participating In An Aerobics Exercise/ Step Class."

RESPONSIBILITY TO RECOGNIZE AND ALERT INSTRUCTOR OF RISKS

For your own safe participation, you must call to the attention of the Instructor any situation which you perceive to be a potential risk or danger to you. Such risks or dangers may include, and are not limited to (a) characteristics of the environment of the location where you perform your program which may pose potential for harm; (b) experiencing unusual difficulty, pain, or other similar sensations in performing a skill or task in this class, and (c) simply not feeling well, fatigue, or being otherwise unable to perform any skill or task in this class. These, and all risks should be brought promptly and clearly to the attention of the Instructor when you suspect them to exist.

SAFETY REQUIREMENTS

Your instructor will give you safety rules you are required to follow. These will include, but are not limited to (a) wearing proper, loose-fitting attire; (b) wearing an appropriate athletic sport shoe with cushioned heel and thick supportive arch. You may, from time to time, be given other directions concerning your clothing, and

protective gear, and you must understand that your failure to abide by these criteria or requests may result in risks to you.

EXERCISING HEART RATE

Your instructor will educate you in how to monitor your own exercising heart rate ("training zone"). It will be your responsibility to exercise only as strenuously as required to attain your training zone and thus enable you to receive the benefits of the training effect. The responsibility to know, and monitor your exercising heart rate is your responsibility.

If your physician has suggested or prescribed any limitation whatsoever upon cardiovascular activity, of course, it is your responsibility to monitor and limit your activities within those limitations. It is your responsibility to consult your doctor, and determine your safe, proper training zone, and your further responsibility to advise the instructor of it.

By now you have already completed the Student Information Profile and Student Physical Activity Readiness; it is your responsibility to make sure that your instructor has been fully advised of any and all medical, psychological, or other emotional conditions which you suspect may in any way limit you in full participation in this course.

GOOD JUDGMENT, ASSUMPTION OF RISK OF LOSS

This course and the physical training tasks and skills which it incorporates require that at all times you use good judgment and that you participate safely. In the event that any injury or loss be incurred during participation with and in this class, it is your responsibility to assume, and pay, and save and hold this University and your instructor harmless from any and all cost, loss, damages, or other claim or demand arising from your participation.

You are advised to make sure that you are covered by a plan of medical care and hospitalization insurance.

QUESTIONS

Never hesitate to ask a question concerning any part of this course.

MEDICAL EXAMINATION: WRITTEN PERMISSION

A thorough medical examination is the recommended way to make sure that your current state of physical health and well being, and your physical capacity are adequate to safely engage in this course.

If you have refrained from regular physical activity for a long time, have recently had surgery, are obese, or have specific limitations, you must obtain a physician's written approval to start participating in this course.

If you are 35 or older, and are otherwise healthy, you still must obtain written permission to participate.

This program is not meant to be a substitute for a cardiac rehabilitation program. If you have been treated for cardiovascular or pulmonary disease, you must obtain written permission from your physician, including a detailed description of your limitations, and your prescription for exercise.

HIGH RISK STUDENTS

It is impossible to isolate and identify what characteristics in your life style and medical history make you a "high risk" student. However, if at least one of the following factors is present, you must advise your instructor of it and, you must not begin this course without the written permission of your physician: (a) if you smoke, or have smoked cigarettes; (b) if you have an at-risk cholesterol reading; (c) if you have known high blood pressure; (d) if you have an abnormal resting ECG; (e) if you have diabetes mellitus; (f) if you have any family history of coronary disease before, or by, age 50.

CONCLUSION

You have now read and understand your responsibilities as a student enrolled in this course. This course is designed to help you; but if you do not perform your responsibilities, this course may well be harmful to you.

With this in mind, your signature below indicates that you have read, totally understand, are willing to, and have abided by, performed, or will perform each and all of the student responsibilities set forth above.

_____   _____
                    Signature   **Date**

V. Aerobics/Step Training Course Syllabus

Abbreviation of University
Name of Course
Number of Course
Date form was developed

Instructor:
Office Hours:
Office:
Phone:
Mailbox:
Phone Messages:

Course Description:

Aerobics/Step Training 100/200 is a motivational course in which the *healthy* student, through active participation, will develop knowledge and skills sufficiently adequate to provide ENJOY-MENT for these cardiorespiratory activities to become personal, lifetime, recreational fitness activities.

Course Objectives: Upon completion of this course, the student will have:

1. Further developed:

   a. aerobic capacity and subsequently vastly improved the individual's cardiorespiratory system (the most important kind of fitness).

   b. strength and flexibility to all muscle groups of the body which will enable the student to have a COMPLETE FITNESS conditioning and training program.

   c. agility, rhythm, coordination, good positioning, and a flair for movement expression all day long!

2. Further improved the student's TOTAL health through understanding (we've mentioned the physical — here's the emotional, intellectual, spiritual, social, and talent expression aspects):

   a. the fitness mindset.

   b. stress management and relaxation techniques.

   c. positive eating strategies.

   d. weight management techniques, including body composition assessment.

e. the unique personalities who are sharing this Aerobics/Step Training class with you this term, through reinforced social interaction.

Course Evaluation:

1. 100 students will receive only an "S" – satisfactory — or "U" – unsatisfactory and will count as one of the requirements for graduation.

   200 students will receive only letter grades — A, B, C, D, F — and is an elective course.

   Scale is as follows:

A	=	Superior work
B	=	Excellent work
C	=	Average work for a college student
S	=	Average or above work
U	=	Below college level work
D	=	Below average work
F	=	Failure to meet requirement

2. Evaluation based upon (see Chart on the next page):

   a. Charted personal data requested:
      ▶ Completeness of the charts.
      ▶ Neatness and accuracy of methods.
      ▶ On-time for date requested.

   b. Attendance: Maximum cuts allowed.

   c. Exam score.

	A	**B**	**C or S**	**D / U**
a.	Superior	Excellent	Average	Below
b.	3	3	3	4
c.	≥ 90%	80-89%	70-79%	60-69%

Course Requirements:

1. Have completed the Student Information Profile and Student Physical Activity Readiness form and turned them in to the instructor your first day of class.

2. Must have read, signed, and turned in the form, Responsibilities of Student Participating In An Aerobic Exercise/Step Training Class. If you are injured in class, please report it to me *immediately!*

3. Dress/Equipment:
   a. Shoe — one that provides for forward and lateral movement, and has a cushioned arch and well-cushioned heel, i.e., an "athletic sport" or "cross-trainer" shoe.
   b. Dress according to your exercise comfort. I prefer that you "dress in layers" and wear a sweat suit, and shorts / tee shirt, or leotard / Spandex® or tights for maximum movement ease. ALWAYS wear or bring DRY athletic shoes. No rain/snow/wet shoes allowed on this floor, ever. Long, tight jeans are unacceptable.
   c. The use of 1-4 lb. hand-held weights can be used, but only *after* I've given an explanation on how/when/and who can use them. They are only optional for the course.

4. Regular attendance. A maximum of three absences/cuts is permitted in this class. I DO NOT EVALUATE CUTS. Simply, if you are not here it is one cut. If you come in after I've taken attendance, it is your responsibility to come up to me and advise me of your

presence. Attendance presence begins the first day of class or the day you enroll/add the class. If you come in after attendance, or leave early, you receive just 1/2 credit for attendance that day, since arriving late and/or early departures are considered disruptive to the meaningful learning going on by others.

5. Purchase the text, *Fitness Through Aerobics & Step Training* (available at the University Bookstore) and keep the following data on your progress (__ total charts/tables):

   (List all charts and tables of monitoring to be collected).

   a. All charted data requested will be turned in on _____(due date)_____. Please *staple* them together *in numerical order listed above.*
   b. An EXAM over information you are asked to read and understand will be given (date of exam) , our last class meeting.

Course Structure and Details:

1. This *Aerobics/Step Training* class will be taught by demonstration, mini-lectures, participation, and audio/visual aids, with group participation in all phases.

2. Upon arrival in class, you will immediately *go to your assigned attendance position* with your textbook and pencil each class meeting.

3. Let's make this an enjoyable 30 hours of *Aerobics/Step Training* together! In order for this course to be of maximum benefit to you, you must continue your program 1–3 EXTRA days per week, time and location optional!

VI.   Course Objectives

The following objectives identify what the students should accomplish during their time in class and are listed to give you direction for categorizing individuals in a mixed class.

AFFECTIVE

Beginner	Intermediate	Advanced
Appreciation of aerobics and step training as two excellent lifetime fitness activity choices.	Understands the need for maintaining and continually improving one's physical condition by regularly practicing the proper techniques given.	Understands that physical inactivity has a negative impact on one's physical and emotional wellness.
Respect for individuals' differences in fitness level and motor skill level, and that progression in each area will greatly vary among participants.	Has the ability to correct common mistakes when learning new moves, when they are pointed out.	Appreciates aerobics and step training as two activities with unlimited possibilities when it comes to choreographing new combinations.
Understands the need to use safe equipment and keep it in good repair (i.e., bench, bands, and tubing) and to wear the appropriate shoes and apparel for a safe workout.	Are able to vary intensity and impact in relation to both the program segments and to meet the individual's needs.	Appreciates the value of an instructor who cues well both visably and audibly, and who can create fun, challenging routines and combinations, either planned or freestyle (spontaneous improvisation).
Understands the need for good positioning and technique in order to have a safe program.	Understands that for safety reasons, one must choose hand weights that are of the proper weight and an easy type to use with the strength segment of the workout.	

COGNITIVE

Beginner	Intermediate	Advanced
Understands all of the responsibilities of being a student participant in a high intensity, low impact fitness class.	Knows how aerobics and step training are categorized.	Can re-structure negative emotions, attitudes, and beliefs into positive images, self-talk, and movements.
Can identify the five total fitness components.	Understands all of the ways to vary intensity.	Can accurately equate their heart rates felt, with their rates of perceived exertion felt.
Understands the five criteria that are necessary for an activity to be labeled aerobic, the benefits of aerobic exercise, and the kinds of modalities that are considered aerobic.	Knows how to correctly lift, lower, and carry a bench.	Can analyse and correct good body position for all segments of a workout.
	Knows the directional approaches/orientations of step training.	Understands the elements of choreography variation.
Can identify the four segments of an aerobic exercise class.	Understands the anatomical names of muscle groups and exercises to use that effectively train them.	Can choreograph balanced, safe, and challenging aerobics routines and step training patterns.
Knows how to take and record own pulse and figure own RsHR.	Understands the need for structuring the integration of positive mindset affirmations into the stretching and strength training segments of a workout.	Understands the principles for strength training and the variety of equipment ways to apply this fitness component in own aerobics or step training workouts.
(Continued)	*(Continued)*	*(Continued)*

COGNITIVE (continued)

Beginner	Intermediate	Advanced
Can readily calculate own TZHR.	Can explain proper eating strategies and their own daily consumption patterns.	Understands the difference between the health fitness standards and the high physical fitness standards in terms of body composition.
Can convert own training zone HR into both a 6- and 10-second count reading.	Understands the weight management principles of gaining, losing, and maintaining lean and fat weights.	Can design an effective total fitness program for self and the general population (i.e., those with no limitations).
Knows how to choose a bench height.		

PSYCHOMOTOR

Beginner	Intermediate	Advanced
Can demonstrate correct body alignment, both static and dynamic.	Can demonstrate exercises to stretch the major muscle groups.	Can continually adjust to using the proper intensity to meet the challenge of the changing beats per minute of the music which accompanies the various segments of the workout.
Can perform sustained low-impact aerobics for a minimum of 20 minutes.	Can perform sustained low-, moderate-, and high-impact aerobics for a minimum of 20 minutes.	Can perform sustained low, high, high/low, and moderate impact aerobics interchangeably, and remain in own target heart rate training zone.
Can perform the three base steps and the basic step training steps.	Can demonstrate the variation step patterns involving travel moves, repeaters, and propulsion moves.	Can perform complete routines of aerobics, multiple-skill step training sequences, and any advanced aerobics or step training choreography presented.
	Can perform two different step patterns sequentially.	Utilizes full range-of-motion arm movements throughout, using the appropriate number of reps for high-range.
	Utilizes low/mid-range arm movements throughout workout.	Uses the maximum number of block risers for step training that own body size requires for safety.
	Can incorporate strength training exercises into workout using tubing, bands, or light hand-weights for weight training isolation work.	Can comfortably add 1-4 lb. hand-weights throughout step patterns for 20 minutes.
	Can integrate relaxation into the cool-down stretching and finish a workout with a heart rate that is lower than before the workout began that session.	Can relax for 3 minutes at conclusion of workout and record a heart rate at or lower than your resting heart rate average.

VII. Identifying Student Skill Level And Rate Of Progression

Here are suggestions for identifying a student's level and rate of progression.

Beginner: A regular exerciser who has never performed aerobic exercise-dance or step training.

Intermediate: A regular participant of aerobics and step training.

Advanced: A skilled and regular aerobics and step training participant.

Skill Level	Impact/Platform Height	Skill Recommendations Steps	Arms
Beginner	Aerobics: Low-impact.	All grounded steps.	Low- or mid-range.
	Step Training: Up to 6".	No propulsions. Base steps. Basic step patterns.	No arms/or limited use. Bilateral. Single action. Low-range.
Intermediate	Aerobics: All impacts.	According to needs & limitations.	All levels.
	Step Training: Up to 8".	Basic step patterns with increased range. Multiple step combinations. Limited propulsions.	Unilateral. Multiple action. Mid-range.
Advanced	Aerobics: All impacts.	Can freestyle-sustained, spontaneous, improvisation.	All levels.
	Step Training: Up to 12".	Advanced step combinations. Propulsions with hops & jumps.	Unilateral. Opposition. Multiple action. Upper-range.

VIII.   Aerobics & Step Training Knowledge Pre-Test/Survey

Note: Pass out computer "bubble" answer sheets to each student. Place name and attendance position on form. All answers are either true or false. Mark true responses as column "a" and the false responses as "b." Explain that the purpose of this survey is to determine the students' knowledge/interests so that the course can be designed to fit their needs.

Answers:

1. T	6. T	11. T	16. F	21. T	26. F	31. F	36. T	41. F	46. T
2. F	7. T	12. T	17. F	22. F	27. F	32. F	37. F	42. T	47. T
3. T	8. F	13. T	18. F	23. F	28. F	33. T	38. T	43. T	48. T
4. F	9. F	14. T	19. T	24. T	29. T	34. T	39. F	44. T	49. F
5. T	10. T	15. F	20. F	25. T	30. F	35. F	40. T	45. F	50. Should be T

★★★

1. A "problem solving strategy" consists of how we perceive, store, and retrieve information, and in that order.
2. The three predominant senses we use to problem solve are sight, hearing, and smell.
3. We self-talk to ourselves 100% of our waking hours.
4. The two controlling forces that direct our lives are our need to delay pleasure and to experience pain.
5. Your attitude can be directly experienced by logging your self-talk.
6. If we are to behavioral change our choices, we ultimately must update our no longer useful beliefs.
7. The basic building blocks of motivation are images, self-talk, and emotion-filled movements.
8. The recommended formula for how much to eat and the time of day for eating should follow the "25-25-50" rule.
9. Good body position and body composition mean the same thing.
10. Efficiency in processing oxygen is called aerobic capacity.
11. Training effect means the total beneficial changes that occur with a proper exercise program.
12. The minimum number of exercise sessions recommended per week to workout is three to experience positive changes in heart and lung fitness, and four to efficiently metabolize body fat.
13. Distress from illness, injury, or test anxiety will all significantly raise resting heart rate readings.
14. Target heart rates and training zone heart rates are synonymous.
15. The three variables to figure into your training zone are age, sex, and resting heart rate average.
16. Of the three means of monitoring and quantifying exercise intensity, the least scientific method used is the rate of perceived exertion.
17. Moderate impact aerobics and combination impact aerobics are two ways of describing the same form of impact.
18. On the Cooper Fitness Run/Walk Tests, the labels defining having physical fitness are "fair," "good," and "excellent."
19. On the Cooper Fitness Run/Walk Tests, the labels defining the lack of physical fitness are "fair," "poor," and "very poor."

20. A power pace-walk is an example of high-impact aerobics.
21. Strength training and weight training are synonymous.
22. When using the resistance tubing, it is a more advanced initial position to use just one foot securing it underfoot, than using two feet spread wide apart securing it.
23. Ballistic stretching is the most common and most acceptable form of stretching to improve flexibility.
24. During pace-walking, the heel of the shoe contacts the ground first.
25. The proper length of a jump rope to use is to have it reach under both arm-pits while standing on the center of it.
26. Sports orthotics are an effective form of hand-held weights.
27. The proper lifting and lowering of the step bench is performed using the strong lower back muscles, and bending from the hips.
28. Marching is a form of high-impact aerobics.
29. Hops and jumps are two forms of high-impact aerobics.
30. "Health fitness" and "high physical fitness" are two synonymous labels used when describing your current body composition classification.
31. When choosing a bench height, the knee should advance beyond your toes as you step up on the platform.
32. Limit the number of power/propulsion moves to one minute.
33. Place your whole foot on the platform when you step up.
34. Step aerobics is an effective fitness workout equivalent cardiovascularly to running 7 mph, while having the impact of walking at a 3 mph pace.
35. Step aerobics is a high impact/low intensity activity.
36. Directional approach/orientation refers to the direction your body faces the bench.
37. Single lead steps should be performed for a minimum of one minute.
38. The step touch base step can be either a single or alternating lead step.
39. If the bench is kept at one consistent level, all of the step moves have been found to expend the same amount of caloric energy.
40. Bilateral arm movements refer to movements that are performed in unison.
41. When performing an alternating lead 4 count basic step pattern using the V-Step or Straddle Down, the 4th step is weight bearing.
42. Intensity can be increased or decreased to accommodate your individual needs.
43. Limit step pattern variations that include high impact (propulsion) moves to 8-16 counts.
44. Adding 1-4 lb. hand-weights increases intensity.
45. Step aerobics is always a low-impact activity.
46. Step aerobics focuses on the major muscle groups in the lower body.
47. Step aerobics provides sufficient cardiovascular demands needed to attain cardiorespiratory fitness according to ACSM guidelines.
48. The bench/step may be used for strength training exercises.
49. Nutrient density principles identify the best food choices we can make are those with the one star rating.
50. I currently exercise vigorously (for at least a minimum of) three days per week, as prescribed by the American College of Sports Medicine.

IX.   Attendance-Taking Made Easy

Accurate attendance taking for 60 students (via this form) can be easily performed *in less than one minute* with this "spot check" method. Assign each student a floor space location to where they are to go each time, upon their arrival to the classroom/gymnasium, after they have discarded their extra belongings (books, coats) along the walls.

To this assigned attendance position is brought only the textbook, a pencil, and the requested equipment for the course (all then stored under the bench when not using these items or along the walls if step-benches are not used).

Where an empty spot is present, that student is marked ABSENT in the grade book at the time attendance is taken. Inform students on the very first class meeting that it is *their responsibility* to come up to you *after class* and alert you of their late presence. Otherwise, they are considered "absent" that day. Allow for no exceptions — this format teaches taking responsibility and accountability for their own time management.

While taking visual attendance, always vocally state first names of students in each position, to blueprint remembering who they are and to re-locate anyone who is in the wrong attendance location in the beginning. This method allows you the freedom of getting to know your students' names much faster and you never have the embarrassment of mis-pronouncing last names that are difficult to pronounce.

If attendance is a key factor in your course evaluation and you feel that certain individuals may be taking advantage of the ease of attendance format by having the tendency to leave early (for the remainder of the hour, during a water/ restroom break need), a re-grouping at the end of the workout hour, back to the attendance position for another spot check, takes only another minute of class time.

Assigning this position can be facilitated in one of two ways: (1) the students choose the spot they wish to always have for attendance and exercising in; or (2) directly via the class roster, alphabetically, front-to-back and then left-to-right of the room. Any students who add the course after the positions are alphabetically assigned, are simply given positions at the end, on the right side of the room. This allows you to record informational data on each student from day one.

For class management purposes, *it is easier to use the alphabetized format*. If students (and/or you) prefer to have them workout in another position in the room after attendance, a warm-up jog (with text/pencil/light equipment in hand) once around the room can be performed, ending with the students assuming any location they then prefer to be in, for the remainder of the hour. Many times, however, the alphabetized attendance format and then keeping that location for the hour provides not only the opportunity for the student to make permanently located new friends, but also a comfortable security in the very large group setting.

	1	2	3	4	5	6 / BACK
1	•Amy Adams 1/1 •Diabetic •+8/20 •Fair •Beginner	1/2	1/3	1/4	1/5	1/6
2	2/1	2/2	2/3	2/4	2/5	2/6
3	3/1	3/2	3/3	3/4	3/5	3/6
4	4/1	4/2	4/3	4/4	4/5	4/6
5	5/1	5/2	5/3	5/4	5/5	5/6
6	6/1	6/2	6/3	6/4	6/5	6/6
7	7/1	7/2	7/3	7/4	7/5	7/6
8	8/1	8/2	8/3	8/4	8/5	8/6
9	9/1	9/2	9/3	9/4	9/5	9/6
10	10/1	10/2	10/3	10/4		10/6

FRONT (left edge, rows 1–10) / BACK (right edge)

Key: 10/6 (Floor Space)
NAME:
LIMITA-TIONS:
PRE-TEST SCORE:
FIT. TEST LEVEL:
COURSE LABEL:

X.   Self Management: "What Do You Say, When You Talk To Your Self?"

STEP I. ASSESSMENT

Have you ever listened to your "intrapersonal" communication? We talk to ourselves 100% of our waking hours and our internal dialogue is either positive and enabling, or negative and disabling to us.

What do YOU say when you talk to yourself? Become aware and listen to yourself for an hour, a day, two days, or a week, and write your internal dialogue statements (both positive and negative) as shown in the examples.

Our self-talk usually takes the form of "I" statements followed by: "am / enjoy / hate / fear / think / feel / want / need / worry about /" etc.

Examples:

▶ "I enjoy Peter and his attention to details."

 "I have been such a klutz! I've dropped everything today."

▶

▶

STEP II. EVALUATION

After you've recorded your Self-Talk for up to one week, go back and evaluate each comment as positive or negative. Circle the ▶ preceding the comment, if it was negative Self-Talk.

Totals: + = _____ – = _____

STEP III. RE-PROGRAMMING

After awareness, the next step in re-programming a negative disabling attitude expressed through your self-talk is accomplished by updating and actually *re-wording each negative statement* you wrote down so that each reads as positive and enabling to you. This opens a main channel for you to begin to achieve your goal of attitude improvement.

1. A listing of negative language you are replacing includes all of the following past or future tense verbs and adverbs (i.e., in regards to personal attitude and fitness mindset improvement): need to, want to, ought to, should, could, wish, used to be, and was.

2. Re-write each of the predicate phrases, using positive, *present-tense* language (I am; I enjoy; I can; and use verbs with "ing" on them as much as possible) and state them *as if* you have *already achieved* the outcome of the new script you're choosing to program.

Example: Old: I need to quit smoking.
          New: "I *enjoy being* a non-smoker."

3. You can *add another* helpful line or two, to each new script, if you wish.

Example: Old: I need to cut out eating high fat, high salt, and highly sugared foods like cookies, for snacks when I get hungry mid-morning at work.

New: I enjoy selecting a highly nutritional, low calorie snack like fruit or juice when I get hungry at work mid-morning. *I feel better about myself every time I make this better choice.*

4. It is best to state positives of positives. However, if you choose to add the negative because you think it will help, place it as the second or *last sentence* of your new script.

Example: Old: I need to exercise more than once a week, and eat less junk food like donuts.

New: I am exercising 3 miles everyday and enjoy being a "fat-burner" instead of a "fat-storer." *I never eat FAT PILLS (donuts) any more!*

5. Be very *specific* as to the outcome of each new scripts' goal. Tell your brain exactly what you want and are now choosing to do.

Example: Old: I enjoy exercising to improve my health.

New: I enjoy exercising for *40 continuous minutes, 4 or more days every week,* to continue achieving my goal of *dropping a pound of body fat a week.*

STEP IV. MAKING YOUR OWN RE-PROGRAMMING-FOR-IMPROVEMENT TAPE ON YOUR BEHAVIORS, EMOTIONS, ATTITUDES & BELIEFS.

The development of your very own "Tape Talk" tool can prove to be one of the most influential and quickest ways for you to achieve changes you're choosing to make. Here are the details.

1. Purchase a good, blank audio-tape cassette that is at least 30 minutes in length on a side. Give it an interesting title!

2. Review your self-management self-talk assessment and take note of some of the most used negative self-talk ideas or phrases you use. Steps I/II/III). Select 15-18 re-programmed scripts (Step III) to tape.

3. The new programmed scripts you tape can also be re-worded beliefs/philosophies that you now choose to adopt, that haven't "stuck" yet. Remember to use positive, present tense language throughout.

4. Take your written-out, prepared new scripts, and on the tape, repeat each of the suggestions 3 times, with a short pause in between each suggestion.

5. Repeat this procedure for each new script. (If you have 15 new scripts, there will be a total of 45 suggestions; if you use 18 new scripts, there will be 54 new suggestions.)

6. End the tape session by recording each of the phrases/scripts one more additional time each, but this time change "I" to "You." This provides for the external validation that we all need to have. The total number of scripts on your entire tape will now be the total of 60/72.

Example: "I am a good listener and enjoy hearing what others have to say" becomes . . . "*You* are a good listener and enjoy hearing what others have to say."

7. If at all possible, add appropriate instrumental music while you tape. Soft, pulsating music seems to affect the way the brain receives and permanently stores information. In order to do this, you'll need an additional tape player, playing the music on it separate from your taping instrument.

8. Talk your scripts onto your tape with emotion! Any programming you currently have in your head is and has been more permanently etched if you experienced it in a highly emotional state.

9. Remember to enjoy re-working your thoughts in language you will enjoy hearing! This is a lot of fun, and just wait until you begin experiencing the results! It is exciting how quickly it can all happen, if you are faithful in playing your tape with regularity.

10. Play your tape while you are doing something else — getting ready each morning, during a break while you are relaxing, during a drive in the car to or from class or work, or as you are getting ready for bed. Play it once or twice a day the first three weeks; then once a day until you realize . . . I've mastered these! It's time to make a new tape on other new challenges!

XI. A Step Training Planning Page For Instructors

1. _____ 9. _____
2. _____ 10. _____
3. _____ 11. _____
4. _____ 12. _____
5. _____ 13. _____
6. _____ 14. _____
7. _____ 15. _____
8. _____ 16. _____

1. _____ 9. _____
2. _____ 10. _____
3. _____ 11. _____
4. _____ 12. _____
5. _____ 13. _____
6. _____ 14. _____
7. _____ 15. _____
8. _____ 16. _____

1. _____ 9. _____
2. _____ 10. _____
3. _____ 11. _____
4. _____ 12. _____
5. _____ 13. _____
6. _____ 14. _____
7. _____ 15. _____
8. _____ 16. _____

1. _____ 9. _____
2. _____ 10. _____
3. _____ 11. _____
4. _____ 12. _____
5. _____ 13. _____
6. _____ 14. _____
7. _____ 15. _____
8. _____ 16. _____

XII.-A   Cueing Techniques

When teaching aerobics and step training it is important to effectively communicate to your students the steps and arm movements being used *in advance of performing the movements* so that your students can easily make the appropriate adjustments and/or changes. This prompting system is referred to as cueing. Cues should be timely, and consistent. Because students have different learning styles, using a combination of *verbal* and *visual* cueing will allow for smooth transitions.

Verbal cues alert students who cannot see the instructor. **Verbal** cues are used to describe the move, count the number of repetitions and other information the instructor would like to relay to the students such as safety precautions/reminders and explanation of moves to come. **Visual** cues are also useful and allow the instructor to give directions without straining the vocal cords.

The following are tips to use for verbal and visual cueing:

VERBAL CUEING

Note: Explanation and understanding of terms and signals used is necessary for verbal cueing to be effective.

1. During the last few beats of the previous phrase *identify the next step and arm movements by name.* Example: "step out wide with claps," "alternating tap up with bicep curls."

2. Describe the *action of the step.* Example: "up, up, down, down;" "point and tap four left."

3. *Count down the last four steps* before changing the steps or arm movements. Example: "last 4, last 3, last 2, now . . .," or count the number of repeaters before changing to the other leg.

4. *Explain the next step or movement* before counting down. Example, "Continue grapevines and after 4, change the knee lifts to kicks."

VISUAL CUEING

Note: To effectively and safely lead a class, the instructor should face the class and provide a mirror image. Facing the class allows the instructor to monitor students' technique and body alignment.

When using visual cueing it is important to use the appropriate orientation to the class. Certain patterns are easier to follow if the instructor and students face a certain direction. For example, when performing the step training straddle and/or lunge moves, each half of the class can face the center.

1. Place hand on hips to indicate a transition or change from one move to the next.

2. Hands and arm gestures can be used to indicate the direction students will be moving or the number of repetitions. Examples: Circle the hand over head for a turn step; point in the direction students will be going when performing traveling moves such as slides; or over the top and across the top bench steps.

3. Ask students to continue jogging in place or stepping and watch the instructor demonstrate the next move.

SUMMARY

Verbal and visual cues are essential in smooth transitions. They are most effective when the instructor can easily be seen and heard.

XII.-B   Cue "Q" Signs*

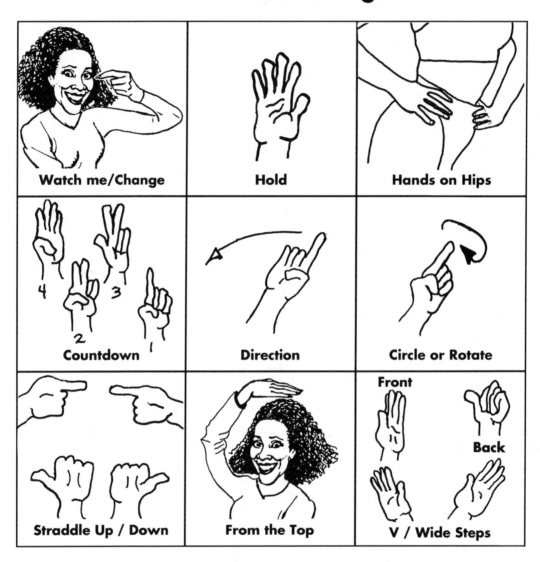

Watch me/Change	Hold	Hands on Hips
Countdown	Direction	Circle or Rotate
Straddle Up / Down	From the Top	V / Wide Steps

* Some ideas from Tamiless Webb, "Step 'Q' Signs," IDEA Fitness Renaissance Educational Conference and Fitness Expo, Pittsburg, PA, 1991.

XIII. Designing Aerobics/Step Training & Strength Training Circuit Workouts

Circuit training involves performing various activities at pre-arranged stations in a pre-determined time-frame of approximately 1-2 minutes. Circuit training combines the benefits of cardiovascular exercise with muscular strength and conditioning. In addition, circuit workouts offer variety for all fitness levels!

When designing a circuit workout it is important to consider the students' fitness goals. Circuit training can provide significant improvements in aerobic capacity, muscle endurance and body composition. Students interested in improving cardiovascular fitness and weight loss should perform a circuit with an emphasis on the *cardiovascular component* (Example 1); while students interested in improving muscle endurance and/or strength will focus more on *resistance training* (Example 2).

Special Considerations

▶ Prior to teaching a circuit workout class, demonstrate the correct form and technique for each exercise to be performed in the circuit.

▶ This format works best when students are familiar with the steps or when experienced students can pair up with beginners.

▶ Display a card with the name of the exercise to be performed at each station.

EXAMPLE 1 — Cardiovascular/Resistance Training

Class Design:

▶ Set up 15 stations around the room (10 cardiovascular and 5 resistance stations). When step training is used, the number of benches and equipment (weights or tubing) at each station will depend on the number of students in the class (for 30 students there should be 2 benches at each station).

▶ Alternate two cardiovascular stations with one resistance. Benches should be adjusted prior to class to accommodate various fitness levels or positioned for the appropriate exercise (incline, decline or flat).

Class Format:

▶ Begin with a 5-10 minute warm-up. This allows the instructor to demonstrate any moves prior to beginning the circuit.

▶ Students can begin at any station. Exercises will be performed for one minute at each station, 15 minutes to complete the circuit, and the circuit may be repeated to extend the length of the workout.

▶ Choose 10 different (a) aerobics segments, (b) basic step patterns or simple step combinations, or (c) a combination of both aerobics and step training stations. Alternate (a), (b), or (c) with 5 strength training exercise stations.

EXAMPLE #1
Aerobics & Step Training with Strength Training

A E R O B I C S

1] Bounce 'n Tap (4 Reps) Series; high- and/or low-impact.
2] Grapevine with touches, knee lifts, kicks, jumps, and hi/low/side claps.
3] Hop, skip, jump, leap series/ and power walks.
4] Polka with variety arm moves/ and jazz touches side and forward.
5] Hopscotch forward and back series, with big arms/ and marching.

S	1] Step training Base steps.
T	2] Alternating Bypasses knee up; kick forward;/side;/back.
E	3] Straddle Up and knee Lift Repeaters.
P	4] Turn Step and Over the Top.
	5] From the End.

S	1] Bicep Curls.
T	2] Tricep Kick Backs.
R	
E	3] Lateral Raises.
N	
G	4] Upright Rows.
T	
H	5] Gravity-Assisted Curl-Ups.

Encourage students to add variations to the basic moves.

EXAMPLE 1

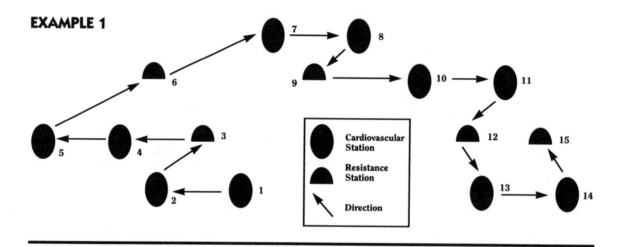

EXAMPLE 2 — Resistance Training

Class Design:

▶ Set up 10 resistance stations around the room. The number of steps and equipment (weights, tubing, or bands) at each station will depend on the number of students in the class.

▶ Steps should be positioned for the appropriate exercise (incline, decline or level).

Class Format:

▶ Begin with a 5-10 minute warm-up.

▶ Students should perform approximately 8-12 repetitions at each station working at 2 seconds per concentric and 4 seconds per eccentric phase (6 seconds per repetition).

▶ The number of cycles performed depends on the length of the workout (i.e., 10 stations × 3 complete cycles = 36 minutes).

EXERCISES #2

1] Bent-Arm Chest Cross-Over (Fig. 7.63)
2] Overhead Press (Fig 7.75)
3] Deltoid Lateral Raise with Squat (Fig. 7.68)
4] Upright Row (Fig. 7.69)
5] Tricep Kick Back (Fig. 7.74)
6] Bicep Curl with Squat (Fig. 7.72)
7] Gravity-Assisted Curl-Up (Fig. 7.76)
8] Back Extension (Fig. 7.78)
9] Reverse Curl-Up (Fig. 7.77)
10] Seated Lower Leg Flexor and Extensor (Fig. 7.84).

Variations:

▶ Type of exercises performed (i.e., all upper body, all lower body, 2 upper/1 lower body, etc.).

▶ Alternate symmetrical/asymmetrical arm movements.

▶ Change the speed of repetitions (2 per concentric and 2 per eccentric).

▶ Vary the number of exercises (8-10) and/or number of cycles.

▶ Vary performing exercise with hand-held weights, bands, tubing, with and without the bench.

EXAMPLE 2

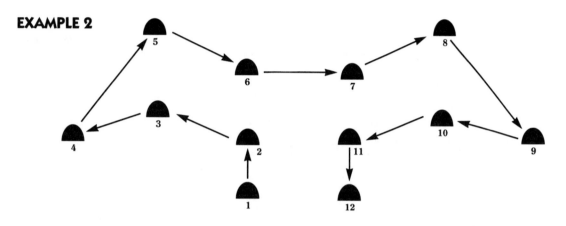

Circuit Summary:

As students progress, vary the circuit by changing the exercises at each station, number of times the circuit is repeated, pace, length of time at each station and/or adding heavier hand-held weights to the step training movements (maximum of 4 lbs.). Be creative; circuit training can add fun and variety to your workout.

XIV. Motivational Theme Classes

After a class has learned the basics involved in aerobics and step training and the related total fitness information, it will then be the opportune time to present creative variety and change in the lessons, in order to sustain the psychological challenge that will be needed.

One motivational option is to present "theme days" in which you change the classroom environment, your appearance or apparel, the music, or add props to coincide with an appropriate theme designated ahead of time for that day. You'll find that theme days are great "community builders" and provide a natural means of encouraging social interaction — one of the course objectives mentioned in the syllabus.

The following suggestions will get you started on themes that are fun to experience in a fitness class setting.

Theme	Apparel/Appearance	Music	Steps/Gestures
All Sports Day	Your attire depicts your favorite sport.	College fight songs.	Karate punches & chops, swimming strokes, ball sport moves.
Hat Day	Wear your all-time favorite hat.	Songs related to the the hats you choose to wear for class.	Tip hat, take it off/on during chorus of song.
Career Day	Prop, hat, and/or tee shirt relates to your career major.	"Working 9 to 5" by Dolly Parton; "Workin' For a Living" by Huey Lewis and the News.	***
Current Affairs	Select a hero or cause and dress, or prop is appropriate.	***	***
Colors	Dress totally in favorite one color — be a crayon. Black tape at cuffs of shirt & sweats.	"The Rainbow Connection."	If this song is used, use for strength training or as a cool down.
Western	Cowboy hat.	"William Tell Overture" (Lone Ranger's Theme).	Pistols.
Favorite Cartoon/ Movie Hero	Batman 1/2 mask and all black; Mickey/Minnie Mouse ears.	"Batman Theme"; "Mickey Mouse Club Theme Song."	***
Collegiate Mascot or Colors day (Homecoming)	Wear your school colors, or impersonate your school mascot.	Your school's fight song.	Cheer punches, or mascot moves.
Holidays (New Years 1/1)	Party hats/horns, sparkly outfit.	"Tiny Bubbles", by Don Ho.	***
Valentines Day (2/14) or Sweetest's day (Sept.)	Hearts/cupids, red w/ white lace; Valentine's decor.	"Love is a Contact Sport." by Whitney Houston or "Lay all Your Love On Me" by ABBA.	Community build by having students touch w/ high-5's, hand-shake during the transitional, on the floor moves; exchange workout stations (have all benches be low height); cupid/archery moves.
St. Patrick's Day (3/17)	Green shamrock, leprechaun.	"When Irish Eyes are Smiling"; "Unicorn."	***
Easter	Bunny cottontail, blackened nose and whiskers, or ears.	"Bunny Hop" by Warren Covington.	On the "hop, hop, hop" chorus perform step touch repeaters.
First of summer	Beach clothes, sunglasses.	Any song by The Beach Boys.	Swimming stroke arms.
Fourth of July	Red, white and blue, straw hat, flags.	"If You Knew Sousa," by Royal Philharmonic Orchestra; "Yankee Doodle Dandy," by Geo. M. Cohan.	Salutes, two victory signs (V) with both fingers and arms.
Labor Day (First Monday in September)	Hard hat, any prop that is work related.	"Get a Job!" by the Silhouettes.	***
Halloween	Creativity is endless! Require charactering on this day.	"Addam's Family Theme"; "Monster Mash," by Bobby "Boris" Pickett.	Add sounds: boo, howl. Ghost and monster steps and gestures.
Thanksgiving	Pilgrim hats, turkey, red beard.	"In the Mood," by The Hen House Five Plus Two; "The Chicken Dance," instrumental.	Chicken walk, chin in/out elbows flapping; Chicken Dance hand gestures.
Christmas	Red reindeer nose, antlars, white tail; Santa beard, hat, belt, and leg warmers.	Instrumental of Rudolph; Santa's Comin' to Town; 12 Days of Christmas.	Ho-ho-ho's; fingers counting down the days of Christmas and gestures for each day.

Some ideas from **Julie Platus, "Theme Classes,"** *IDEA Today*, Nov.-Dec., 1988.

XV.   Body Composition Assessment By Skinfolding Technique

SECTION A: Determining Your Percent Body Fat. Record your three skinfold readings, add them together, and record total value.

_____   (men: chest; women: triceps)

_____   (men: abdomen; women: suprailium)

_____   (men: thigh; women: thigh)

_____   Total of 3 skinfold readings for: _____
                                                                                                 Student's Name

Using Table 11.1, 11.2, or 11.3, determine your current percent body fat according to your age

and gender and record it here: _____

SECTION B: Determining Recommended / Ideal Body Weight.

1. **Fat Weight:** Multiply your total body weight in pounds (BW) by the current percent fat (%F) you're carrying (see Section A), expressing this percentage in decimal form. (BW × %F). This is your fat weight (FW), the actual number of pounds of fat you now carry. (BW × %F = FW).

2. **Lean Weight:** Subtract your fat weight (FW) from your total body weight (BW − FW). This is your lean weight (LW). (BW − FW = LW).

3. **Select** your desired ideal body fat percentage (IFP), based on your goals and the "health" or "high fitness" standards given in Table 11.4. Express this percentage in decimal form.

    ._____% (IFP)

4. **Recommended / Ideal Weight:** To calculate your ideal weight, use the following formula: LW % (1.0 − .IFP) = Recommended / Ideal Weight (IW).

Example: A nineteen year-old-female who weighs 136 pounds and is 25 percent fat would like to know what her recommended / ideal weight should be, with a "desired" fat percentage of 17%, which is "high physical fitness" standard for her.

Sex: female
Age: 19
BW: 136 lbs
%F: 25% (.25 in decimal form)
IFP: 17% (.17 in decimal form)

GOAL: _____

1. FW = BW × %F
   FW = 136 × .25 = 34 lbs.

2. LW = BW − FW
   LW = 136 − 34 = 102 lbs.

3. IFP: 17% (.17 in decimal form)

4. IW = LW ÷ (1.0 − .IFP)
   IW = 102 ÷ (1.0 − .17)
   IW = 102 ÷ (.83) = 122.9 lbs.

5. To reach her ideal weight, she needs to goal-set to loose 13.1 pounds of fat weight (136 − 122.9 = 13.1).

XVI. Fitness Course Instructor Evaluation of Students / And Student Self-Assessment

KEY:
"4" / A = always
"3" / U = usually
"2" / O = occasionally
"1" / S = seldom
"0" / N = never

Student's Name

Aerobics (Techniques / Skills / Knowledge)

- Know how to determine RsHR.
- Know how to determine TZHR.
- Warm-up exercises are active, medium-to-low level, rhythmic, limbering, standing, full range-of-motion.
- Perform slow, sustained static stretching (no bounce).
- Engage in continuous breathing.
- Exhale during stretch; inhale as release from stretch.
- During low-impact: legs kept low, arms below heart.
- During power low-impact: hip, knee, ankle extending moves are followed by a knee flexion, ankle springing action; one foot always in contact with the floor; space is well used.
- During high/low-impact: higher knees performed, and arms overhead more frequently; both airborne and grounded moves are used.
- During low-impact cool-down: active, rhythmic, full range of motion, but low-level, slower, half-tempo moves are performed.
- Post-aerobic stretching includes: standing stretches for hamstrings, quadriceps, and calves.
- Know how to vary intensity and impacts.

Step Training (Techniques / Skills / Knowledge)

- Know how to select proper bench height.
- Use proper posture - keep back straight, head & chest up, shoulders back, abdomen tight and buttocks tucked under hips.
- Lean forward slightly with the whole body. Don't bend at hips.
- Step up lightly, making sure whole foot lands on platform.
- Do not lock knees when stepping up.
- Step down close to platform, not back.
- Bring heel down to floor before taking next step.
- Avoid excess arm movements over head.
- Maintain appropriate speed for safe movement.
- Do not pivot or twist on weight-bearing leg.
- Maintain muscular balance by working opposing muscle groups.
- Know bench/step directional approaches / orientations.
- Can perform single lead base step.
- Can perform alternating lead base step (w/bench tap, floor tap, lunge).
- Can perform step touch (toe & heel).
- Can perform v-step.
- Can perform straddle down.

XVI. Fitness Course Instructor Evaluation of Students / And Student Self-Assessment (cont.)

KEY:
"4" / A = always
"3" / U = usually
"2" / O = occasionally
"1" / S = seldom
"0" / N = never

Student's Name

Step Training (cont.)

Can perform straddle up.
Can perform single & alternating bypass moves (knee, kick forward kick back, side leg lift).
Can perform lunge (from side & end).
Can perform turn step.
Can perform over the top.
Can perform repeaters.
Can perform propulsion steps.
Limit propulsions & power moves.
Can perform single skill sequence (change one element at a time).
Can perform double skill sequence.
Can perform multiple skill sequence.

Strength

Precede strength training with static stretching.
Joints and spine are stabilized before each exercise.
Smooth, continuous, full range-of-motion movements performed.
Maintain a slow timing, and are not jerky.
Take two seconds to overcome resistance.
Take two to four seconds during release/lowering phase.
Exhale during lifting phase; inhale during lowering phase.
Visualization and self-talk are engaged.
1-3 sets, 8-12 reps format.
Can add 1-4 lbs. resistance.
Brief rest period is taken between bouts.
Can lift and lower whole body against gravity.
Can properly add weight resistance to body part used.
Can control use of hand-held weights.
Can use rubber resistance bands efficiently and effectively.
Can use rubber resistance tubing efficiently and effectively.
Can combine tubing with bench workout.
Can combine step with strength using tubing and the bench in intervals of 3 min. step, to 1 min. strength-with-tubing.

Flexibility

Can slowly actively stretch, with position held at joint extreme.
Can slowly gently press beyond this point without motion.
Can mentally relax, visualize, self-talk, and hold for 15 sec.
Can slowly withdraw from stretch.
Performs to opposite side of body for each stretch.
Can perform at least one PNF stretch.

Relaxation

Can construct powerful images to relax.
Can construct positive self-talk affirmations.
Can deep breathe and effectively lower after-workout heart rate.

XVII. Final Examination Test Questions

1. The three predominant senses are:
   a. taste, smell, and sight.
   b. smell, hearing, and sight.
   c. visual, auditory, and kinesthetic.
   d. visual, touch, and smell.

2. The three action components of a fitness program are:
   a. flexibility, muscular endurance, and body composition.
   b. aerobic fitness, body composition, and flexibility.
   c. flexibility, aerobic fitness, and muscular strength and endurance.
   d. muscular strength, muscular endurance, and positioning.

3. The *main* objective of aerobic fitness training is to:
   a. increase the oxygen supply to all body parts.
   b. lower one's blood pressure.
   c. decrease the body's cholesterol level.
   d. develop lean weight.

4. What is the indicator of true fitness?
   a. Amount of weight you can maximally bench press in one repetition.
   b. Lack of illness.
   c. Condition of heart, lungs, and blood vessels.
   d. Excellent body lean to body fat ratio.

5. The following are aerobic exercises:
   a. jumping rope, yoga, aerobics.
   b. swimming, rowing, strength training.
   c. bicycling, flexibility training, weight training.
   d. running, skating, step training.

6. Among the essential criteria for aerobic exercise are that:
   a. it must be rhythmic and use both the large and small muscles.
   b. it must use the large muscles, be rhythmic, and be maintained in the training zone heart rate.
   c. it must be maintained in a specified target heart training zone for the 80-minute duration of each workout.
   d. it must be done every day to maintain the target heart training zone.

7. Intensity of workouts is measured by:
   a. the skinfold test in conjunction with RPE.
   b. THR training zone and the Siri formula.
   c. consulting standardized height/weight charts developed by the American College of Sports Medicine.
   d. finding the THR training zone, ratings of perceived exertion, and the talk test.

8. The pulse can be taken at:
   a. the carotid artery.
   b. the radial artery.
   c. temporal area.
   d. all of the above.

9. After improving your heart/lung fitness, the resting heart rate:
   a. will become higher during sleep.
   b. will become lower in general.
   c. will show a noticeable difference immediately after waking up.
   d. will fluctuate with seasonal temperatures.

10. Anaerobic exercises:
    a. are done intensely for a short duration.
    b. utilize oxygen to produce energy.
    c. involve flexibility, such as gymnastics.
    d. are synonymous with aerobic exercise.

11. The Borg Scale measures:
    a. resting heart rate.
    b. target heart rate.
    c. high-impact aerobics.
    d. ratings of perceived exertion.

12. High-impact aerobic exercises are characterized by:
    a. one foot remains in contact with the floor.
    b. exercises designed for individuals who are out of shape.
    c. jogging, hopping, and jumping.
    d. faster music and larger moves.

13. Aerobic capacity can be measured by:
    a. skinfold test and a lab fitness test.
    b. a lab physical fitness test or a field test.
    c. skinfold test and posture photos.
    d. a skinfold test and a field test.

14. Pace walking is:
    a. an anaerobic option.
    b. an aerobic option.
    c. the same impact action as jogging.
    d. a flexibility exercise.

15. Flexibility training is effective in:
    a. increasing muscle mass, endurance, and strength.
    b. increasing joint mobility and reducing injuries.
    c. improving exercise performance and cardiovascular fitness.
    d. raising resting heart rate.

16. The push-up is an example of:
    a. a flexibility exercise for the quadriceps.
    b. a plyometric exercise to strengthen the legs.
    c. an aerobic exercise.
    d. a strength activity for the chest.

17. Sports orthotics:
    a. are arch supports.
    b. are worn outside the athletic shoe.
    c. control the foot the entire time it is on the floor.
    d. are shoes with built-in insoles.

18. Proper clothing:
    a. promotes safety, comfort, and ease of movement.
    b. consists of layering in all climatic conditions.
    c. should consist of fabrics that retain heat to hasten weight loss.
    d. should be loose around the ankles to ensure free movement.

19. For muscle strains or sprains:
    a. warm whirlpools are recommended to inhibit swelling.
    b. ice, compress, and elevate.
    c. apply dry heat.
    d. restore body electrolytes by increasing fluid intake.

20. The most common injury of new aerobics exercisers is:
    a. Achilles tendonitis.
    b. bunions.
    c. shin splints.
    d. ankle sprains.

21. Correct lifting entails:
    a. a head-low, raised buttocks position.
    b. forcing the arms to provide the necessary power.
    c. bending from the hips.
    d. an erect back position.

22. Choreography is defined as:
    a. aerobics and gymnastics combined with step training.
    b. movements performed to a 1–3–3–2 count.
    c. the art of designing or planning movements.
    d. costumed aerobics performed to music.

23. "Balanced" choreography has the following components:
    a. music, rhythm, and dance.
    b. dance-exercise, step training, and rhythm.
    c. biomechanical safety and physiological and psychological considerations.
    d. three minutes of step training followed by one minute of strength training.

24. For aerobics, the following surface is considered best:
    a. wood.
    b. carpeting.
    c. mats.
    d. concrete.

25. Nutrient density is:
    a. the weight of food in grams.
    b. measured by the percentage of each of the basic nutrients in one ounce of food.
    c. the relative proportion of fats and cholesterol to other ingredients in a serving of food.
    d. the amount of nutrition per calorie each food provides.

26. Grains provide:
    a. the carbohydrates needed for energy.
    b. the protein needed for muscle growth and strength.
    c. the minerals needed for proper electrolyte balance.
    d. the vitamins needed to maintain good health and wellness.

27. One gram of fat equals:
    a. 10 calories.
    b. 6 calories.
    c. 9 calories.
    d. a nutrient density of 8.0.

28. One principle of weight loss states that:
    a. fat is best metabolized by performing very high-intensity, short-duration exercises.
    b. spot reduction is accomplished by specific exercises for targeted areas of the body.
    c. a light exercise program tends to decrease your appetite.
    d. if you lose water weight, you should try to gain it back within 24 hours.

29. What kind of weight should always be the only type to lose?
    a. Lean.
    b. Fat.
    c. Lean and fat in a 50/50 ratio.
    d. None of the above.

30. The body's _____ determines whether a person gains or loses body fat
    a. electrolyte control mechanism
    b. ratio of fat weight to lean weight
    c. energy balance
    d. absorption rate of vitamins and minerals

31. To decrease your heart rate, when using the bench:
    a. do not use weights.
    b. lower bench height.
    c. increase music tempo.
    d. both a. and b.

32. The energy cost of step aerobics is effected by:
    a. step height.
    b. rate of stepping.
    c. age of participant.
    d. a & b.

33. A regular step trainer should use a bench height of:
    a. 4 inches.
    b. 6 inches.
    c. 8 inches.
    d. 12 inches.

34. A single lead step can be performed from which of the following bench orientations/ approaches?
    a. Front.
    b. Top.
    c. End.
    d. All of the above.

35 Which of the following is a base step?
    a. Alternating lead.
    b. V-step.
    c. Turn step.
    d. Lunge.

36. Bypass moves can be performed as:
    a. single lead.
    b. alternating lead.
    c. a & b.
    d. step touch.

37. Which of the following moves can be classified as traveling moves?
    a. Straddle up.
    b. Bench tap.
    c. Over the top.
    d. V-step.

38. When both feet push off the ground or bench, exchanging positions during the airborne phase it is called a _____ move.
    a. bypass
    b. traveling
    c. turn step
    d. propulsion

39. _____ is a slow, controlled stretch where you gently push or press to the point of tightness.
    a. Ballistic stretching
    b. Static stretching
    c. Proprioceptive neuromuscular facilitatory stretching
    d. None of the above

40. Initial movements onto the bench can begin from all of the following directions **except**:
    a. back to the bench.
    b. standing on top of the bench.
    c. facing the bench.
    d. straddling the bench.

41. When performing a single lead base step (right leg leading), change to a left leg lead by tapping the:
    a. left foot on the bench.
    b. right foot on the bench.
    c. left foot on the floor.
    d. right foot on the floor.

42. When performing an alternating lead v-step the 4th count is:
    a. weight bearing on the bench.
    b. non-weight bearing on the bench.
    c. weight bearing on the floor.
    d. non-weight bearing on the floor.

43. When performing an alternating bypass knee lift the 4th count is:
    a. weight bearing on the bench.
    b. non-weight bearing on the bench.
    c. weight bearing on the floor.
    d. non-weight bearing on the floor.

44. When selecting a bench height do not allow the knee to flex less than:
    a. 30 degrees.
    b. 60 degrees.
    c. 90 degrees.
    d. 120 degrees.

45. When stepping up onto the bench your knee should:
    a. stay aligned over your toes.
    b. stay aligned over your heel.
    c. extend beyond your toes.
    d. lock as you step up.

46. Proper alignment and stepping technique **does not** include which of the following:
    a. abdomen tight.
    b. buttocks tucked under hips.
    c. shoulders aligned over hips.
    d. slight forward bend at the hips.

47. When lifting the bench, **do not**:
    a. bend over from the hips (head low, buttocks high).
    b. keep your back straight.
    c. bend at the hips, knees and ankles.
    d. a & b.

48. Which of the following is **not** an appropriate warm up move for step aerobics?
    a. Bench step taps.
    b. Marching on top of the bench.
    c. Repeaters.
    d. Straddling the bench and alternating taps on top of the step.

49. Following the warm up and stretch phase, participants should perform the:
    a. strength training exercises.
    b. cool down phase.
    c. step aerobics phase.
    d. relaxation phase.

50. The strength training segment of the step aerobics workout should focus on the:
    a. lower body.
    b. upper body.
    c. abdominals.
    d. b & c.

51. Which of the moves listed below **could not** easily follow a base step?
    a. Straddle down.
    b. V-step.
    c. Repeaters.
    d. Knee up.

52. Which of the moves listed below **could not** easily follow a turn step?
    a. Tap down.
    b. Over the top.
    c. Straddle down.
    d. V-step.

53. Which of the following is **not** a consideration when designing or planning movements?
    a. Safety.
    b. Height of step.
    c. Fitness level of participant.
    d. Speed of music.

★★★

ANSWERS:

1. c	9. b	17. c	25. d	33. c	41. c	49. c
2. c	10. a	18. a	26. a	34. d	42. d	50. d
3. a	11. d	19. b	27. c	35. a	43. c	51. a
4. c	12. c	20. c	28. d	36. c	44. c	52. d
5. d	13. b	21. d	29. b	37. c	45. a	53. b
6. b	14. b	22. c	30. c	38. d	46. d	
7. d	15. b	23. c	31. d	39. b	47. a	
8. d	16. d	24. a	32. d	40. a	48. c	

★★★

XVIII. Self Post-Assessment

1. Did you establish a fitness routine outside of class?

2. Retake either a laboratory physcial fitness test ("stress test") or Cooper's Twelve Minute or 1.5 Mile Test.
   ▶ What is your present fitness level (i.e., category)?
   ▶ What change have you experienced over the past 10 (or so) weeks?

3. What was your initial resting heart rate?
   ▶ What is it now?

4. What is your safe exercising zone?

5. How many days per week did you perform:
   ▶ stretching exercises?
   ▶ step aerobics?
   ▶ aerobics?
   ▶ alternative aerobic modalities?
   ▶ strength training?
   ▶ relaxation techniques?

6. What exercise prescription (dosage of above) do you plan to continue on a weekly basis?

7. What poor choice/habit have you changed, eliminated, or made great improvement upon mastering it?

8. What new enabling self-talk affimation statement or personal belief are you choosing to have concerning physical fitness?

9. What is your heart rate after three minutes of relaxation technique?
   ▶ How does this compare to your current resting heart rate?

10. On your own, have a post-assessment body composition evaluation performed (i.e., another skinfold measurement taken).
    ▶ Has your lean weight increased or decreased?
    ▶ Has your fat weight increased or decreased?
    ▶ Your present weight "category" is:

11. Take a look at your daily consumption of food.
    ▶ Realizing your good and not-so-good eating (intake) habits, have you improved your diet any, since this pre-assessment was first made, to include having it now be more nutritionally balanced?

12. What needs to be present, to insure a lifetime fitness commitment?

13. List your top 10 priorities in rank order of their importance to you.
    1. _____   6. _____
    2. _____   7. _____
    3. _____   8. _____
    4. _____   9. _____
    5. _____   10. _____

14. Goals I'm setting for myself:
    ▶ Short-term:

    ▶ Long-term:

XIX.-A   *Fitness Through Aerobics & Step Training* Course and Instructor Evaluation

University Name / Department Name / Course Number
Course Name / Term / Year
Instructor's Name

I liked:

I disliked:

The instructor's good qualities:

The instructor could improve upon:

If I were teaching this course I would:

Would you ever consider taking a Fitness Through Aerobics and Step Training course:

_____ from this instructor again?

_____ as another one of your required physical education courses?

_____ solely as an *elective* (you are permitted ___ electives)?

Do you feel the objectives stated for this course were met? Explain. (Objectives stated on your syllabus were to develop cv fitness, strength, flexibility and other physical skills; understand fitness mindset; stress management through lecture and relaxation; understanding positive eating strategies and weight management; and social interation with classmates.)

Which aerobics routine/step training pattern did you enjoy most this term? _____
Is this a "one term" thing with you, or do you think these are activities that you will continue to enjoy as lifetime ways of staying physically fit?

Write any additional comments on the back. Thanks for your constructive criticism. This is how I improve the course for future students. Have a nice break!

_____
(Instructor's Signature)

XIX.-B Fitness Course & Instructor Evaluation (by Students)

Background Information:

Gender: _____ Female.   _____ Male.

Age: _____ 15-20 yrs.   _____ 21-30 yrs.   _____ 31-40 yrs.   _____ 41-50 yrs.   _____ 50+ yrs.

_____ Student.   _____ Faculty/Staff/Alumni.   _____ Other.

What fitness class do you attend:

Day _____   Instructor _____   Term _____

Hour _____   Classroom Location _____   Year _____

	Strongly Agree	Agree	Undecided	Disagree	Strongly Disagree
The routines are well organized and easy to follow.	5	4	3	2	1
The sessions are fun, creative, and enjoyable.	5	4	3	2	1
The instructor provides information on safety principles, body alignment, etc.	5	4	3	2	1
The instructor is enthusiastic and motivating.	5	4	3	2	1
The instructor gives clear directions and cues that can be heard throughout the class.	5	4	3	2	1
The instructor is prompt and begins the class on time.	5	4	3	2	1
The instructor provides modifications and encourages the class to work at their own pace.	5	4	3	2	1
The volume of music is appropriate.	5	4	3	2	1
The speed of the music is appropriate for the different class sessions.	5	4	3	2	1
The music is motivating and enjoyable.	5	4	3	2	1

If you have checked disagree or strongly disagree on any question above, please comment:

Additional comments regarding this Fitness Class or Instructor:

THANKS

XX. Resources: Music / Books / Journals / Videotapes / Equipment

The following list of resources are those I've found to be quite helpful and authoritative when planning a fitness class of this nature.

▶ FITNESS MUSIC

Music provides a signifiant role for it provides the underlying structure of an aerobics and step training program. Fun and exciting music can motivate and challenge the participants. Creating tapes can be very time consuming and costly. There are, however, several companies which are in the business of producing tapes to use for aerobics, step training, and other types of exercise classes. Some of these music companies offer a wide variety of music styles to choose from — pop, funk, top 40, oldies, instrumentals, etc. Many of the tapes also include music for muscle conditioning exercises.

AEROBIC BEAT
Ken Alan Associates Fitness Consultants
7985 Santa Monica Blvd. Suite 109
Los Angeles, CA 90046
(213) 659-2503

AEROBICS MUSIC INC.
P.O. Box 86
Cardiff by the Sea, CA 92007
(800) 748-6372

AEROBIX MIX INLYTES PRODUCTIONS
614 Sherburn Lane
Louisville, KY 40207
(800) 243-PUMP
(502) 894-8008

DYNAMIX
203 Edgevale Road
Baltimore, MD 21210
(800) 843-6499

EXERCISE SAFETY ASSOCIATION
P.O. Box 391466
Solon, OH 44139
(800) 622-SAFE

FIT NET
P.O. Box 2178
San Leandro, CA 94577-0334
(415) 430-2505
(800) 288-BFIT

FITNESS FIRST
P.O. Box 251
Shawnee Mission, KS 66201
(800) 421-1791

FITNESS WHOLESALE
895-A Hampshire
Stow, OH 44224
(800) 537-5512

MUSCLE MIXES
623 N. Hyer Avenue
Orlando, FL 32803
(800) 52MIXES

POWER PRODUCTIONS
P.O. Box 550
Gaithersburg, MD 20884
(800) 777-BEAT

XX. Resources: Music / Books / Journals / Videotapes / Equipment (continued)

▶ BOOKS / JOURNALS / VIDEOTAPES / EQUIPMENT

American Alliance for Health, Physical Education, Recreation and Dance, *Nutrition For Sport Success*, (Reston, VA: AAHPERD) 1984.

American College of Sports Medicine 1990: Position Stand, "The Recommended Quality and Quantity of Exercise for Developing and Maintaining Cardiorespiratory and Muscular Fitness in Healthy Adults." *Med. Sci. Sports Exercise* 22:2, pp. 265–274, 1990.

Connirae Andreas and Steve Andreas, *Heart of the Mind*, (Moab, Utah: Real People Press) 1989.

Lynne Brick R.N. & David Essel, M.S. *Pump 'N Step*, 1991), (Videotape).

Lynne Brick, *Total Body Workout*, (Philadelphia: Creative Instructors Aerobics, 1991), (videotape).

Kenneth H. Cooper, *The Aerobics Program For Total Well Being*, (New York: M. Evans and Company) 1982.

Kenneth H. Cooper, *Running Without Fear*, (New York: M. Evans and Company) 1985.

Candace Copeland-Brooks, *Moves . . . and More!* (San Diego: IDEA, Inc., 1990), (Videotape).

Candace Copeland, *The Low-Impact Challenge For The Fitness Professional*. (Newark, N.J.: PPI Entertainment Group/Parade Video, 1991), (Videotape).

Wayne W. Dyer, *Pulling Your Own Strings*, (New York: Thomas Y. Crowell Company) 1978.

Shad Helmstetter, *What to Say When You Talk to Yourself*, (New York: Pocket Books, Simon and Schuster, Inc.) 1986.

James L. Hesson, *Weight Training For Life*, (Englewood, CO: Morton Publishing Company) 1985.

IDEA: The Association For Fitness Professionals, *IDEA Today*, 6190 Cornerstone Court East, Suite 204, San Diego, CA 92121-3773.

Arnold Lazarus, *In the Mind's Eye*, (New York: The Guilford Press) 1984.

Julie Moo-Bradley & Jerrie Moo-Thurman, *Aerobics Choreography in Action: The High-Low Impact Advantage*. (San Diego: IDEA, Inc., 1990), (Videotape).

Anne Morrow Lindbergh, *Gift from the Sea*, (New York: Vintage Books, division of Random House) 1975.

National Dairy Council, 6300 North River Rd., Rosemont, IL 60018-4233, for *Guide to Good Eating*, 1991 and *Food Power*, 1983.

Greg Niederlander, *Step Strength*, (SPRI Products & Brick Bodies, 1991), (Videotape).

Nutrition Education Services/Oregon Dairy Council, 10505 S. W. Barbur Blvd., Portland, OR 97219, for *Super FOUR*, 1991.

John Patrick O'Shea, *Scientific Principles and Methods of Strength Fitness*, Second Edition (Reading, MA: Addison-Wesley Publishing Company) 1976.

M. Scott Peck, *The Road Less Traveled* (New York: Touchstone Book, Simon and Schuster) 1978.

Anthony Robbins, *Unlimited Power*, (New York: Simon and Schuster) 1986.

Sports Step, Inc., 3200 Professional Pkwy., Building 100, Suite 150, Atlanta, GA 30339, for The STEP™ bench and video accompanying The STEP™, *Introduction To Step Training*, (Atlanta: 1989). For information, 1-800-SAY-STEP.

SPRI Products, Inc. 1554 Barclay Blvd., Buffalo Grove, IL 60089 for resistance bands and tubing equipment and information. 1-800-222-7774.

SPRI Products, Inc. & Brick Bodies, *Step Strength* (Wheeling, IL: SPRI Products, Inc.), (Videotape).

Melvin H. Williams, *Nutrition for Fitness and Sport*, (Dubuque, IA: Wm. C. Brown Publishers) 1988.

XXI. Invitation to Share Research and Comments

After you have previewed the course textbook, *Fitness Through Aerobics & Step Training* and this accompanying comprehensive Instructor's Manual, I'm sure that you will find a wealth of teaching information, methods, and techniques.

I would like to invite your comments and newly published research findings on any and all information presented within. Please send your correspondence to the address below. Thank you for your professional sharing of ideas and research.

Karen S. Mazzeo, M.Ed.
Personal Excellence®
408 Normandie Blvd.
Bowling Green, OH 43402